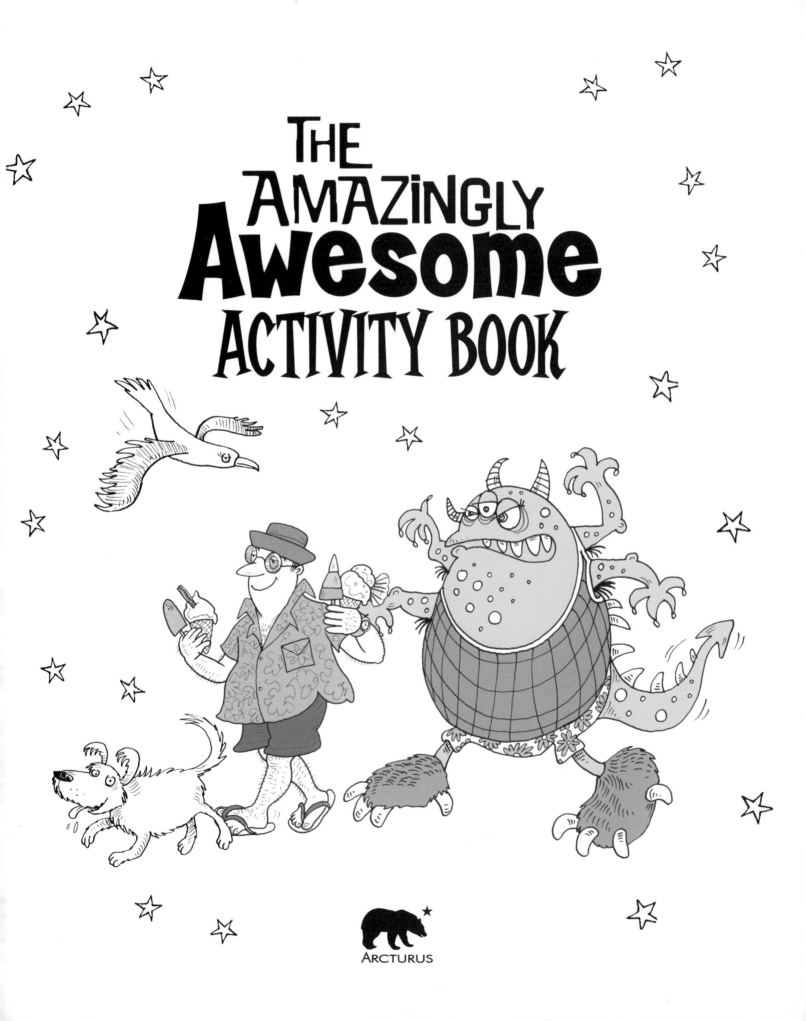

THE AMAZINGLY Awesome ACTIVITY BOOK

ARCTURUS

ARCTURUS

This edition published in 2015 by Arcturus Publishing Limited
26/27 Bickels Yard, 151–153 Bermondsey Street,
London SE1 3HA

ISBN: 978-1-78404-299-8
CH004303NT
Supplier 29, Date 0715, Print Run 4300

Author: Lisa Regan
Illustrator: Beccy Blake
Editor: Kate Overy
Designers: John Walker and Trudi Webb
Additional design by JMS Books

Printed in China

CHEEKY MONKEYS

Which of these monkeys is the odd one out?

CAPITAL LETTERS

Fill in the missing letters to spell five capital cities from around the world. Can you match them to the country they are in?

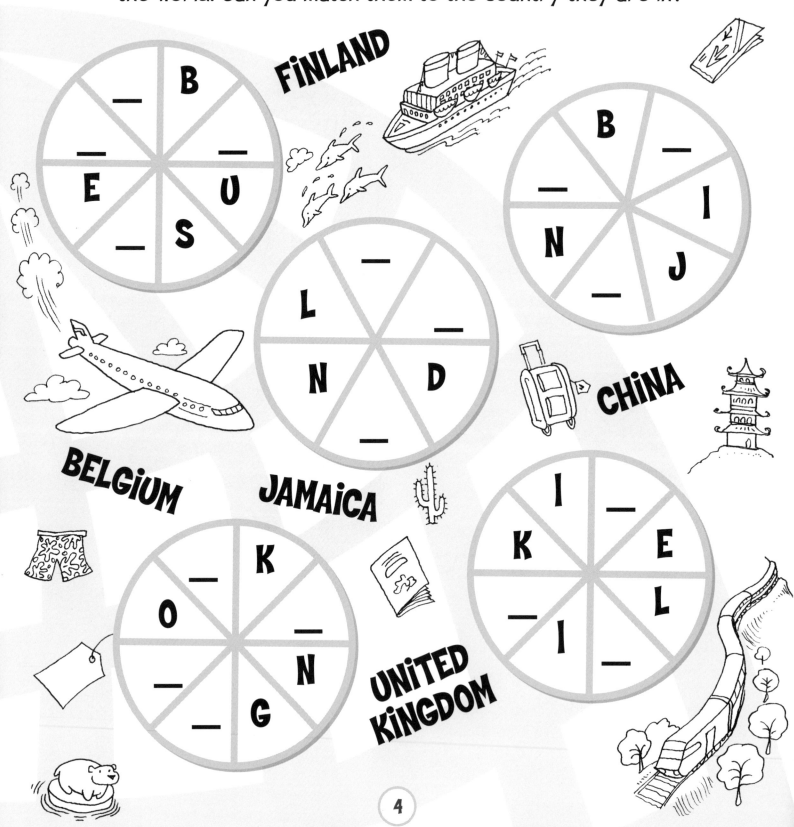

FINLAND

CHINA

BELGIUM

JAMAICA

UNITED KINGDOM

A WALK IN THE PARK

Answer the questions using the grid references from the map.

1. What are people doing in A4 and A5?
2. Which square contains the porcupine?
3. What animals are in squares C1 and C2?
4. Which square contains the swings?

UNDER COVER

Help the soldier through the camouflage net by
following the numbers that are multiples of five.

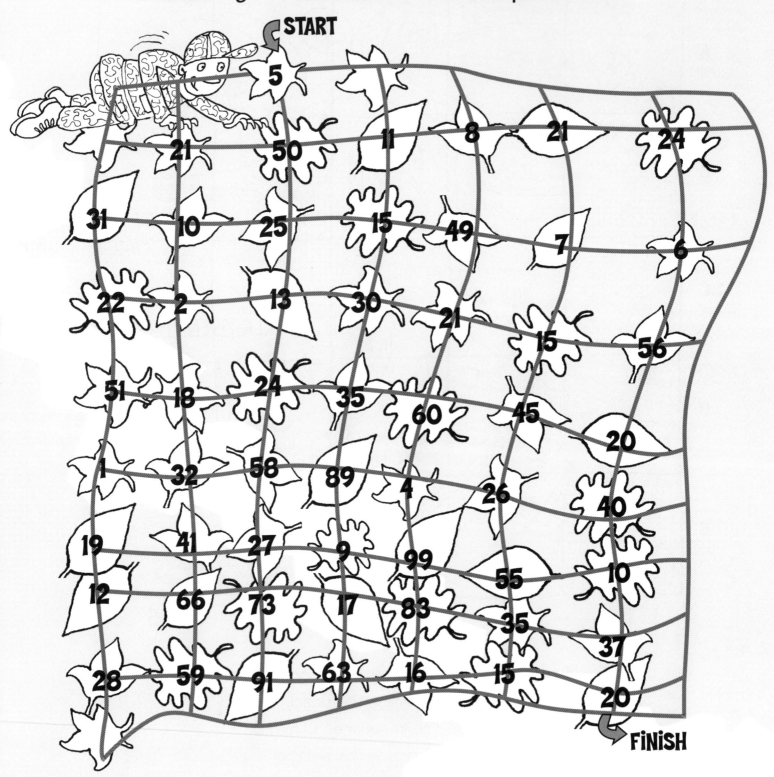

NUMBER CRUNCH

Figure out which number is represented by each symbol to make the equations add up in every row and column.

☰ = ☐ ?

◇ = ☐ ?

✳ = ☐ ?

◎ = ☐ ?

MONSTER MAD

This monster is hopping mad!
But which silhouette matches him exactly?

HAUNTED HOUSE

Can you find your way through the maze to escape from the haunted house? Don't bump into any ghosts along the way!

9

TASTY TREATS

How many frozen goodies are jumbled in this picture?

ANIMAL BREAKOUT

Answer the questions to fill in the code and open the hamster's cage so he can come out and play.

1. How many four-legged creatures can you see?
2. How many birds can you count?
3. How many lizards are there?
4. How many animals have no legs?

Enter code here

PIRATE PARADE

Only two of these pirate pictures are exactly the same.
Can you spot which two?

12

ALPHADOKU

Solve the puzzle so that every row, column,
and mini-grid contains the letters A to F.

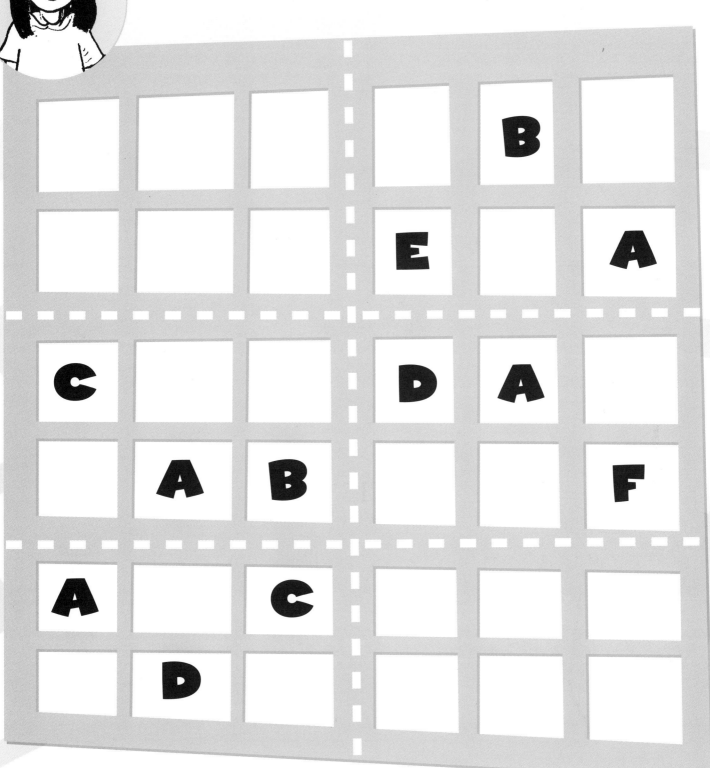

13

SPOT THE DIFFERENCE

There are six differences between these two pictures.
Can you circle them all?

MENU MIX-UP

Match the boxes in pairs to make the names of ten different kinds of food. One has been done to help you get started.

~~BAN~~   ATO   TOM   ~~KEY~~

POT   ORA   SAL   ~~NUT~~   FLE   ROT

PEA   BUR   NGE   ~~ANA~~   ATO

CAR   ~~TUR~~   WAF   MON   ~~GER~~

B	A	N	A	N	A

p	e	a	n	u	f

bu	u	r	g	e	r

T	a	v	k	e	y

WORLD RECORDS

The world is full of amazing places! Can you find some of them in the grid?
Look for the names hidden across, down, or diagonally.

NILE (longest river)

AMAZON (largest river)

EVEREST (highest mountain)

PACIFIC (largest ocean)

GREENLAND (largest island)

RUSSIA (largest country)

CHINA (largest population)

SAHARA (largest hot desert)

R	M	A	M	E	T	C	G	R	E	E	C
U	B	N	A	V	S	P	H	N	A	V	H
S	A	i	i	E	E	A	S	i	M	E	B
N	R	A	S	L	R	C	A	Z	A	S	A
E	A	O	S	O	E	i	H	Z	Z	U	i
E	H	P	U	N	V	F	A	i	O	R	K
R	A	G	R	E	E	N	L	A	N	D	A
G	S	R	C	i	F	i	C	A	P	A	L
M	S	G	R	U	S	E	V	i	H	C	E
A	M	A	Z	S	Z	M	A	C	P	T	V

PLANET SIX

Fill in the missing numbers on the spaceship, counting up by six.

ODD ONE OUT

Which of these toucans is the odd one out?

GRIDLOCKED

The mini-grid only appears once in the larger grid below.
Can you find it?

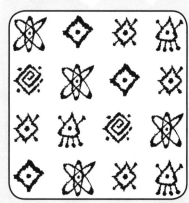

SOCCER SUMS

Which soccer shirt should each player wear?

CLASS ACT

Put your memory to the test by studying this picture for three minutes. Then turn the page to see how many questions you can answer correctly.

CLASS ACT

How much can you remember about the picture
on the previous page?

1. What is shown on the board?

2. Is the teacher a man or a woman?

3. How many children are in the picture?

4. What time is it?

5. What is on the windowsill?

6. How many children are wearing sweatshirts?

7. What classroom pet did you see?

8. How many coats are hanging up?

9. What pattern is on the rain boots?

10. What shape is the pencil case?

FAIRY TALES

How many words of three letters or more can you create from the letters below? Two are listed to help you get started.

ONCE UPON A TIME

1 ___TEAM___

2 ___POTION___

3 _____

4 _____

5 _____

6 _____

7 _____

8 _____

9 _____

10 _____

11 _____

12 _____

SUDOKU

Solve the puzzle so that every row, column, and mini-grid contains the numbers 1 to 6.

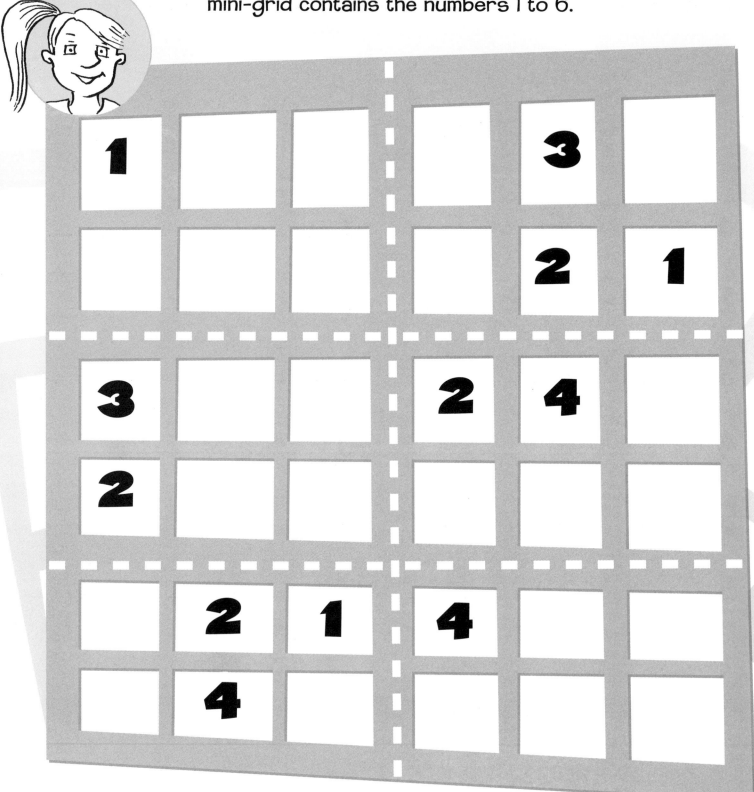

OUT OF ORDER

Can you rearrange the six pictures so that they tell the story in the correct order?

TREASURE HUNT

Follow the directions to find where the Inca treasure is buried.

1. Start in square E5 and walk north for four squares.
2. Head west past the pyramids for three squares.
3. Move two squares south and stop before the llamas.
4. Step one square west. Where is the treasure hidden?

DOUBLE TROUBLE

Starting at the X each time, use every other letter to spell the names of four birds. The remaining letters spell out four more bird names.

27

TIGER TABLES

Help the tiger cub find its mother by counting up in fives,
starting at the number 5.

20	15	10			85	90	95
25	30	START 5			80	105	100
40	35	60	65	70	75	110	115
45	50	55	190	185	170	165	120
210	205	200	195	180	175	160	125
215					150	155	130
FINISH 220					145	140	135

28

DINO-DETECTIVE

The spy has to collect a hidden package from the Dinosaur Museum. Use the code to figure out which exhibit it is hidden behind.

A	✺
B	◉
C	✳
D	❇
E	❄
F	❄
G	✳
H	✳
I	✳
J	✳
K	✳
L	●
M	○
N	■
O	◰
P	◱
Q	◲
R	◳
S	▲
T	▼
U	◆
V	❖
W	◗
X	✸
Y	✹
Z	✺

29

PLANE SAILING

Look at the main picture, and then figure out which of the smaller pictures is the view you would have of the same scene from a plane.

 **a**

 **b**

 **c**

 **d**

 **e**

 **f**

ON THE MOVE

Can you unscramble each set of letters to reveal the transportation words?

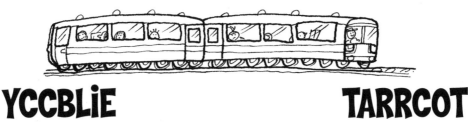

YCCBLIE

TARRCOT

THACY

RANTI

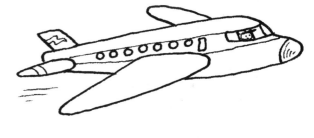

NEAPL

SPOTEDABE

YROCEOTCML

POTLICEHER

FEEDING FRENZY

Chris has bought ice cream for everyone!
But which silhouette matches him exactly?

ZOO SHOPPING

Ben wants to get something from the zoo's souvenir shop.
Answer the questions below to figure out what he can buy.

$2.00 $1.00 $2.50 $0.50 $3.00

$0.75 $4.00 $5.00 $0.30

1. How much will he spend if he buys a baseball hat and a giraffe toy?

2. How many pencils can Ben buy with $3?

3. What costs more: three large elephant toys or two snow globes?

4. If Ben gives the shopkeeper $5, how much change will he get if he buys a large elephant toy, a baby elephant toy, and a card?

ALPHADOKU

Solve the puzzle so that every row, column,
and mini-grid contains the letters A to F.

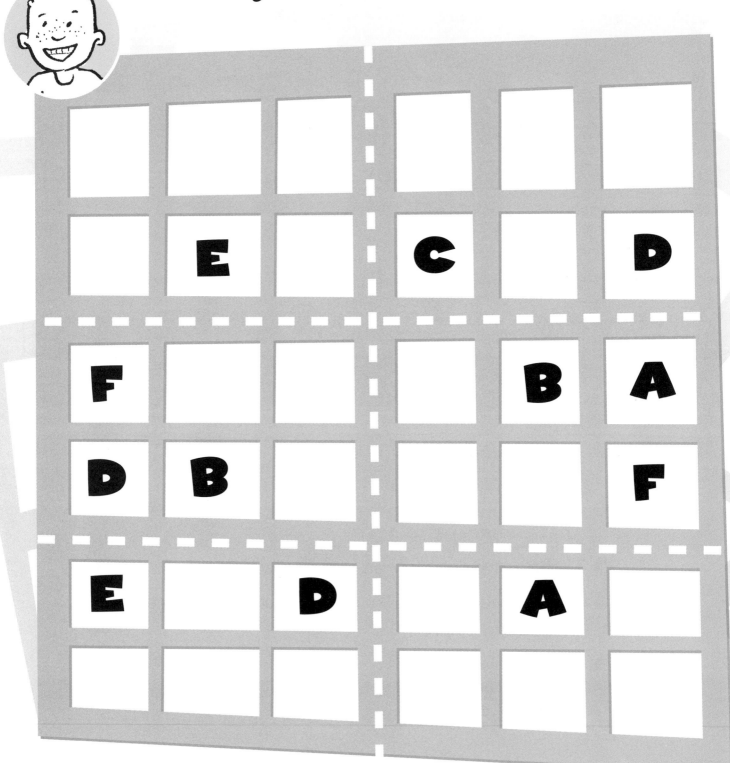

WHAT NEXT?

Study the sequence of pictures carefully.
Which cow finishes the pattern: a, b, or c?

AT THE POOL

Which jigsaw piece finishes the picture:
a, b, c, d, or e?

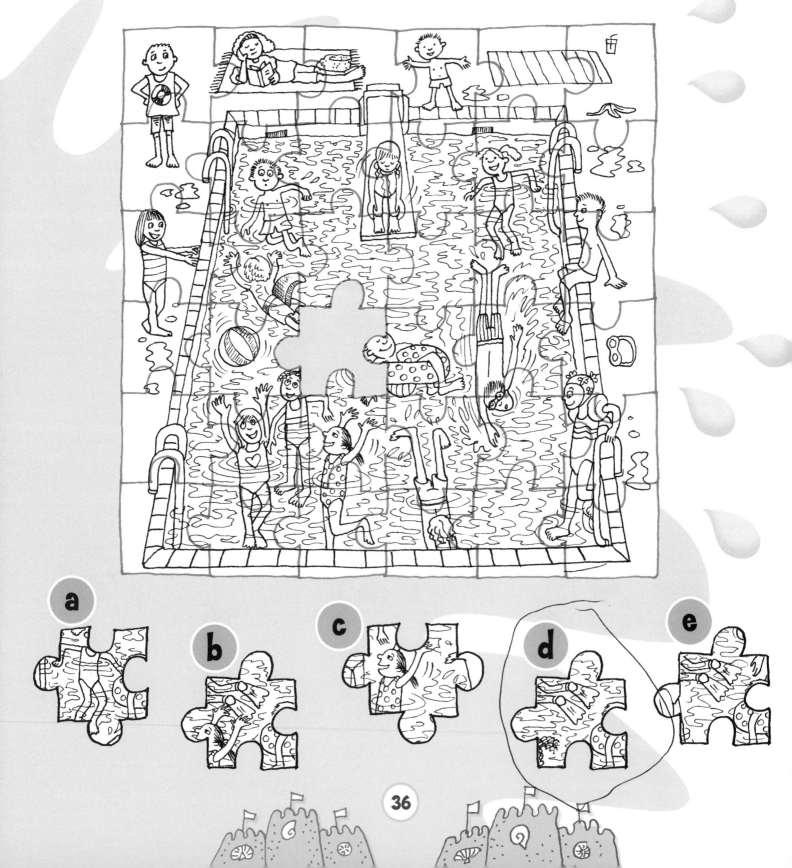

AT THE GAME

Can you spot which six items are different in the two pictures?

BUGOKU

Solve the puzzle so that every row, column, and mini-grid contains each of the four bugs.

MOON WALK

Follow the arrows to guide the astronaut across the planet, without jumping on any craters.

THIRSTY WORK

Which drinking bottle belongs to Joe?
Use the clues to help you work it out.

1. It has a domed lid on it.
2. It has a square label on it.
3. It isn't spotty.
4. It doesn't have a flame pattern.

a

b

c

d

e

f

A DAY AT THE ZOO

These two pictures were taken on a trip to the zoo. Can you see which three people have arrived in the bottom picture?

FOOD FOR THOUGHT

In each grid, cross out any letter that appears twice. The remaining letters spell out three items you might find on a menu.

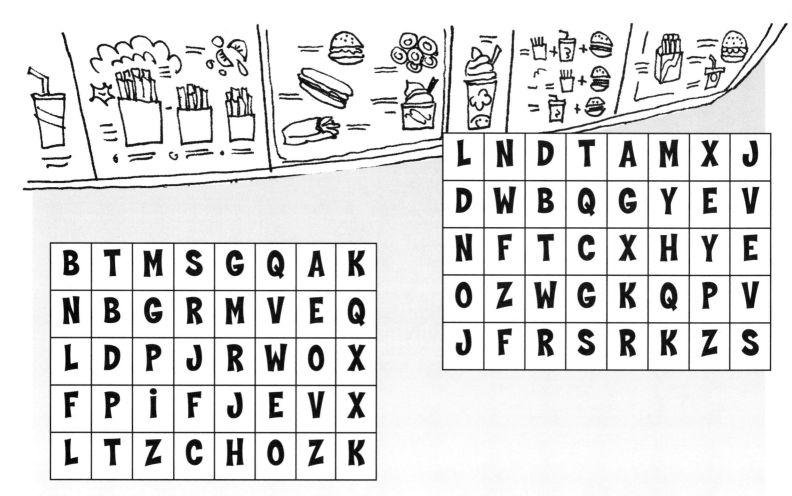

B	T	M	S	G	Q	A	K
N	B	G	R	M	V	E	Q
L	D	P	J	R	W	O	X
F	P	i	F	J	E	V	X
L	T	Z	C	H	O	Z	K

L	N	D	T	A	M	X	J
D	W	B	Q	G	Y	E	V
N	F	T	C	X	H	Y	E
O	Z	W	G	K	Q	P	V
J	F	R	S	R	K	Z	S

B	T	T	J	B	V	F	L
O	i	M	M	J	V	Z	G
X	O	D	Q	S	H	P	P
C	D	R	A	N	Y	Z	G
L	R	K	Q	Y	N	X	E

AT THE AIRPORT

Use your eagle eyes to spot each of the items listed on the left that are hidden in the main picture.

Find these!

GRIDLOCKED

The mini-grid only appears once in the larger grid below. Can you find it?

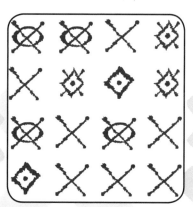

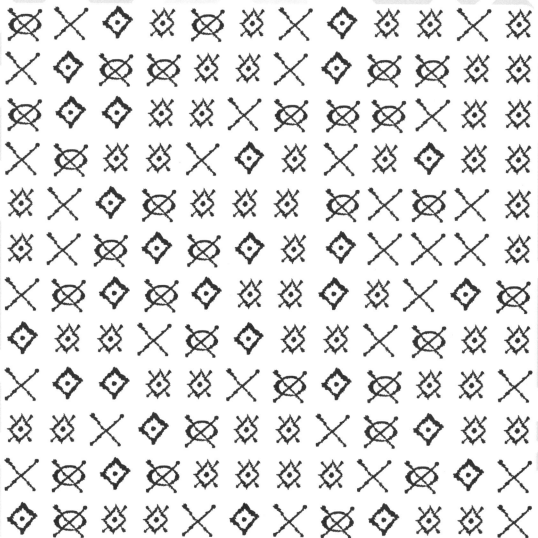

SPY SCHOOL

Use the coded alphabet to find out where the spy is going on her next assignment.

A	✺
B	◉
C	✳
D	❋
E	❅
F	❆
G	✳
H	✳
I	✳
J	✳
K	✳
L	●
M	○
N	■
O	◻
P	◻
Q	◻
R	◻
S	▲
T	▼
U	◆
V	❖
W	◗
X	✸
Y	✹
Z	✳

FEEDING TIME

Answer the questions to fill in the code and let
the zookeeper enter the enclosure to feed the snake.

Enter code here

1. How many enclosures contain lizards?

2. How many legs does a stick insect have?

3. How many frogs are there?

4. How many animals have four legs?

CAMPSITE CHALLENGE

Look carefully at the top picture, and then find the five things that have been changed in the bottom picture.

SPACED OUT

Fill in the missing letters to spell six things that you can find in outer space.

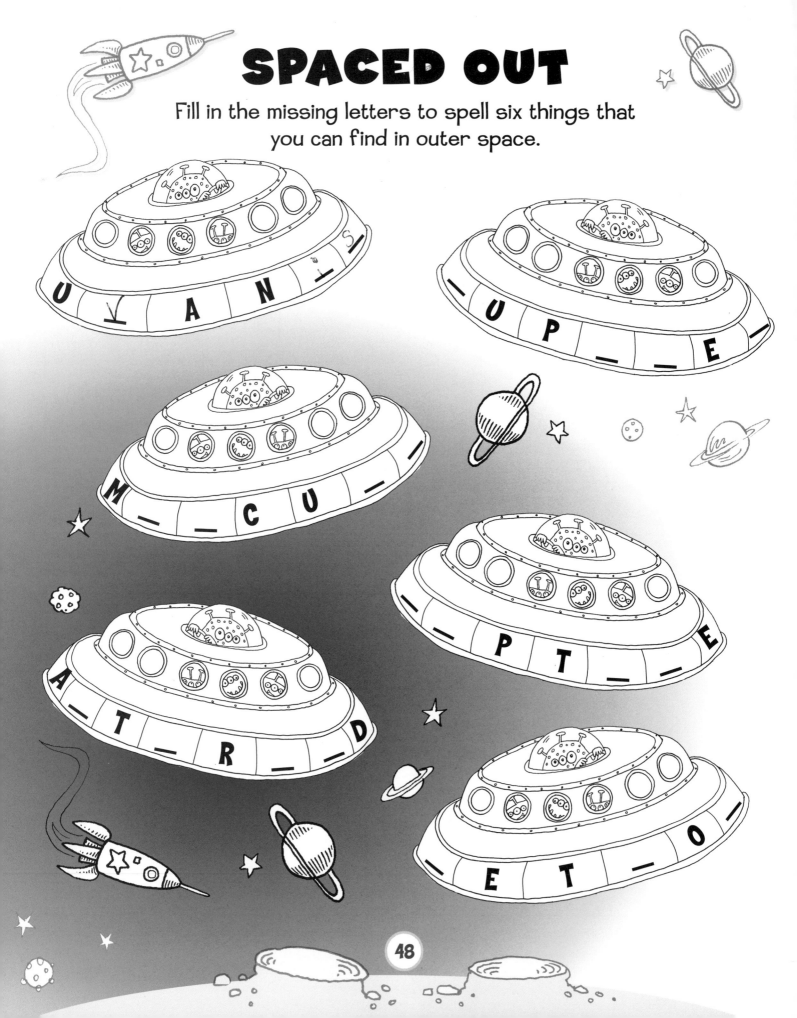

U _ _ A N _ S

_ U P _ _ E _

M _ _ C U _ _

_ _ P T _ _ E

A _ T _ R _ _ D

_ _ E T _ _ O _

BUGOKU

Solve the puzzle so that every row, column, and mini-grid contains each of the four bugs.

SPY SCHOOL

Can you figure out what this message says?

PIECES OF EIGHT

Which jigsaw piece finishes the picture: a, b, c, d, or e?

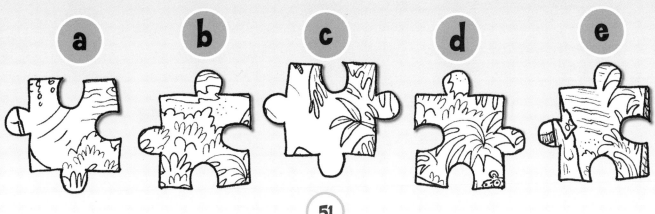

SNACK SUMS

Figure out which number is represented by each piece of food to make the equations add up in every row and column.

🍒	🥧	🍒	🍦	**17**
🍎	🍦	🍦	🍎	**20**
🍦	🍒	🥧	🍦	**16**
🍒	🍎	🥧	🍒	**19**
20	**18**	**15**	**19**	

🍒 = **7**

7		7		**17**
				20
	7			**16**
7			7	**19**
20	**18**	**15**	**19**	

🍎 = ☐ ?

🍦 = ☐ ?

🥧 = ☐ ?

🍦 = ☐ ?

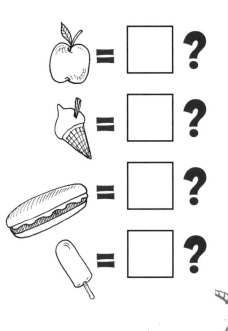

DOUBLE TROUBLE

Starting at X each time, use every other letter to spell the names of four sports. The remaining letters spell out a different activity.

53

FOURASAURUS

This dinosaur loves the number four!
Fill in the missing numbers on its scales.

BLAST OFF!

Which of these space shuttles is the odd one out?

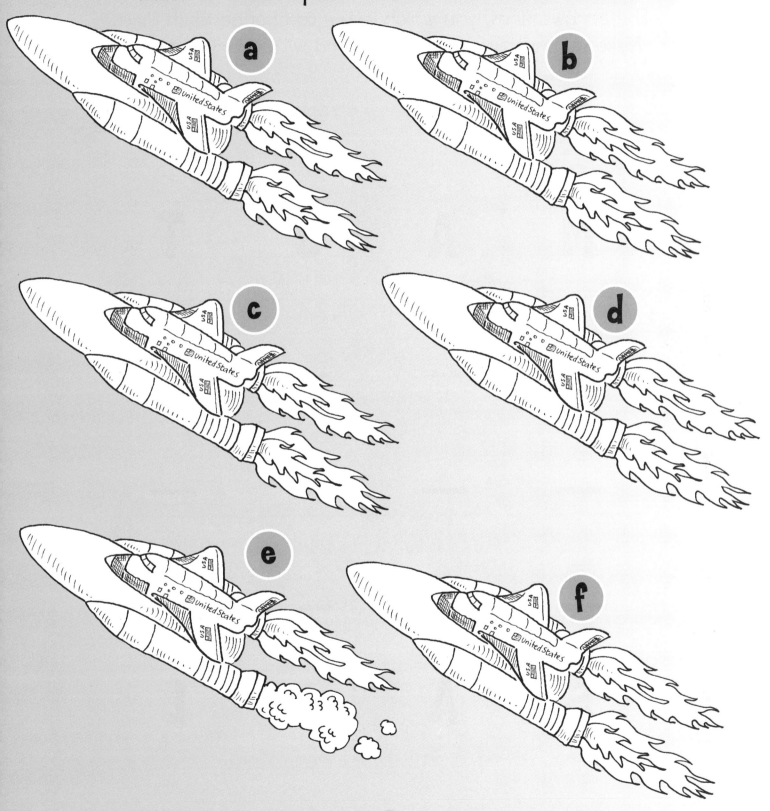

RIGGING RIDDLE

Change the word MAST to the word SAIL one letter at a time.
The arrows show you which letter to change each time.
Make sure you create a real word with every change.

M A S T

_ _ _ _

_ _ _ _

_ _ _ _

S A I L

NUMBER MAZE

Answer the problems correctly to work your way through the grid of numbers.

(5)   13 – 3   (16)   7 x 2   (8)   24 ÷ 6   (5)   7 – 1

START   8 + 3   (14)   4 + 4   (16)   30 ÷ 2   (11)   10 x 1   (1)

(11)   4 x 2   (8)   12 – 6   (19)   18 – 7   (3)   4 x 2

15 ÷ 5   (6)   9 + 7   (6)   10 ÷ 2   (20)   4 x 7   (5)

(7)   1 x 11   (13)   4 x 8   (5)   8 – 2   (16)   6 x 3

6 x 6   (2)   18 ÷ 9   (22)   11 + 11   (40)   9 ÷ 3   (1)

(36)   3 x 4   (19)   20 ÷ 5   (6)   21 – 5   (0)   18 – 11

14 ÷ 7   (5)   30 ÷ 6   (8)   24 – 8   (3)   7 x 5   (15)

(2)   30 – 18   (12)   3 x 3   (7)   13 + 11   (14)   40 ÷ 4

27 ÷ 9   (43)   16 – 7   (9)   8 x 3   (50)   11 x 3   (6)

(9)

FINISH

ELEPHANT RIDE

This elephant is fit to carry a king! But which silhouette matches it exactly?

ANIMAL MIX-UP

Match the boxes in pairs to make the names of ten different animals. One has been done to help you get started.

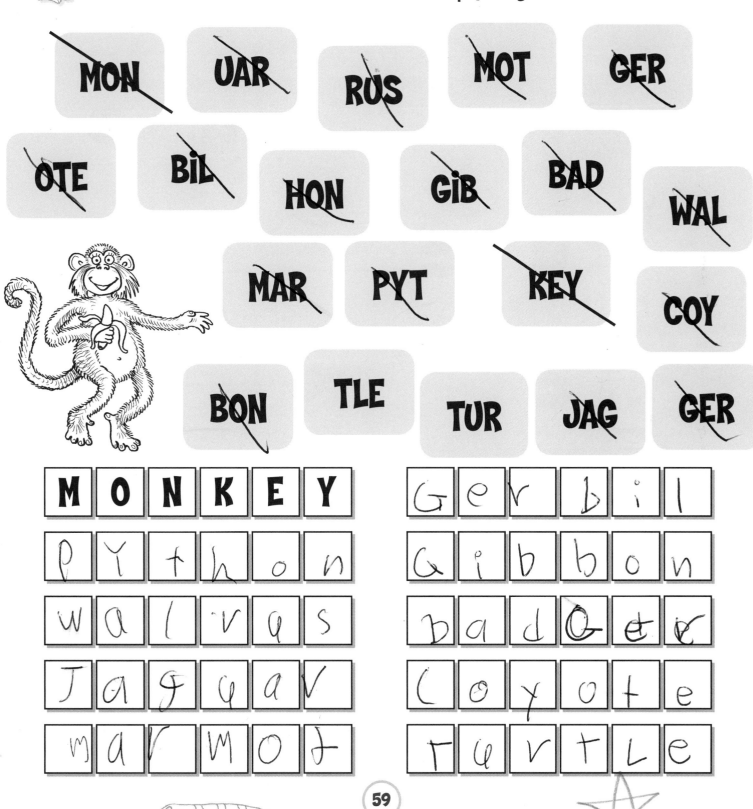

MON | UAR | RUS | MOT | GER
OTE | BIL | HON | GIB | BAD | WAL
MAR | PYT | KEY | COY
BON | TLE | TUR | JAG | GER

M	O	N	K	E	Y
P	Y	t	h	o	n
w	a	l	r	a	s
J	a	g	u	a	r
m	a	r	m	o	t

G	e	r	b	i	l
G	i	b	b	o	n
b	a	d	G	e	r
C	o	y	o	t	e
T	u	r	t	l	e

ALPHADOKU

Solve the puzzle so that every row, column,
and mini-grid contains the letters A to F.

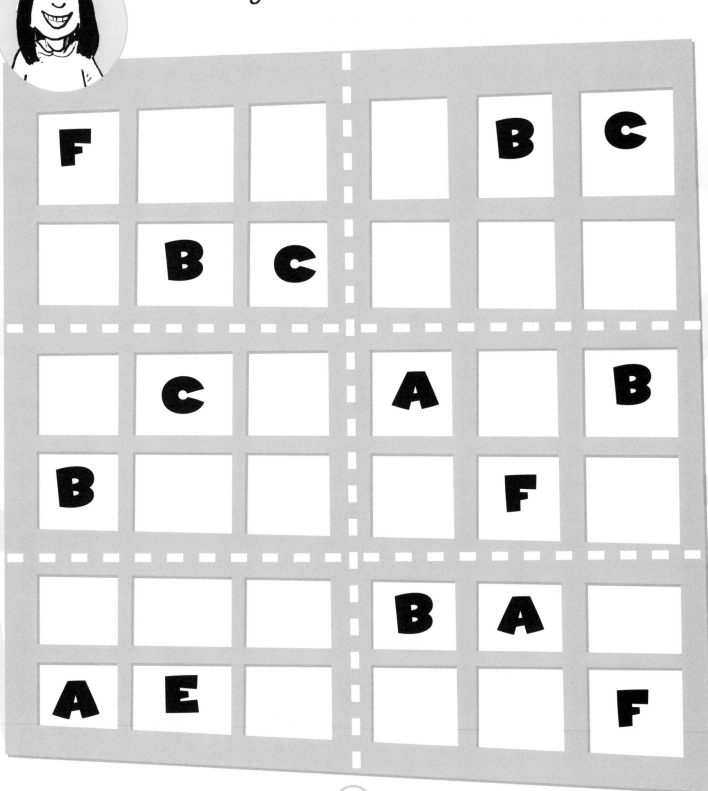

STATION SLEUTH

Test your memory by studying this picture for three minutes. Then turn the page to see how many questions you can answer correctly.

STATION SLEUTH

How much can you remember about the picture on the previous page?

1. How many taxis are waiting outside the station?

2. What time is it?

3. Where is the closest train going to?

4. How many suitcases are on the baggage cart?

5. What is the man on the bench doing?

6. Which way is the arrow on the sign pointing?

7. What is printed on the T-shirt of the man by the train?

8. What is on sale in the store at the back of the station?

9. What musical instrument can you see?

10. What platform numbers can you see?

FAIRY DUST

Only two of these fairies are exactly the same.
Can you spot them?

ENDANGERED SPECIES

Some of the world's most amazing animals are in danger of becoming extinct. Can you find these eight in the grid? Look for the names hidden across, down, or diagonally.

ELEPHANT   **PANDA**
GORILLA   **RHINOCEROS**
LEOPARD   **TIGER**
ORANGUTAN   **WOLF**

E	L	E	R	N	T	L	O	E	P	A	D
L	E	A	A	A	Y	i	D	U	G	X	R
W	O	T	W	T	N	A	G	T	W	E	A
A	X	O	O	U	R	D	U	E	O	C	P
E	L	E	F	G	U	O	A	T	R	Y	O
F	O	L	T	N	A	H	P	E	L	E	E
D	R	E	i	A	O	R	P	H	A	N	L
U	A	S	O	R	E	C	O	N	i	H	R
G	N	R	H	O	O	N	R	H	i	P	O
B	T	i	C	H	E	G	T	A	H	A	Y

A BUG'S LIFE

Help the bug munch its way through the apple maze.

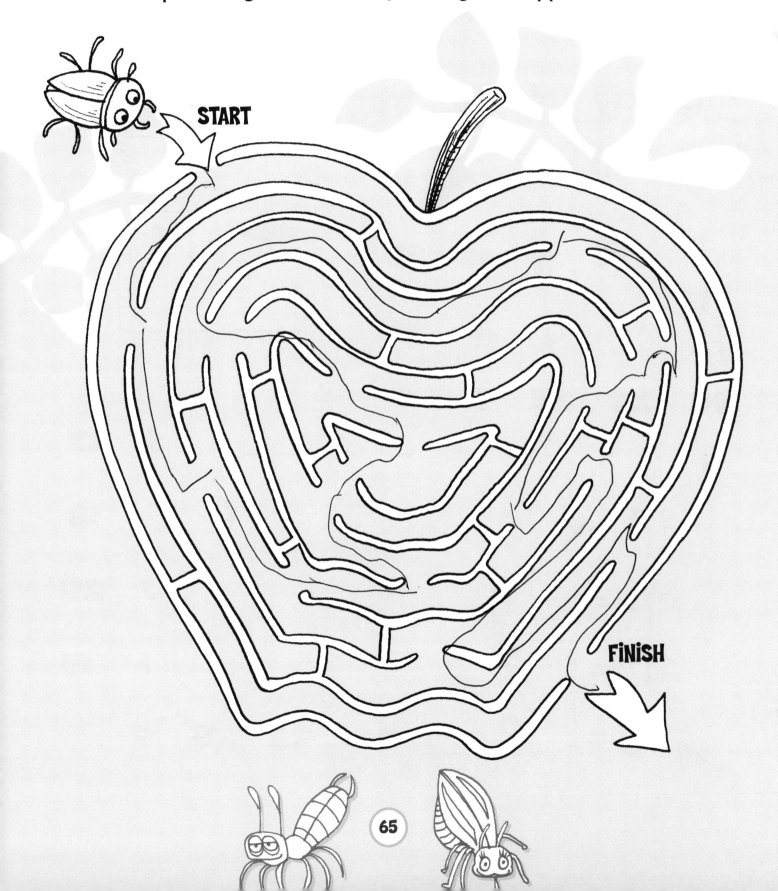

START

FINISH

65

NUMBER CRUNCH

Figure out which number is represented by each symbol to make the equations add up in every row and column.

🍴 = ☐ ?

👼 = ☐ ?

⚓ = ☐ ?

🍍 = ☐ ?

OLYMPIC GAMES

Answer the questions using the grid references on the map.

1. What sport can you watch in D1 and D2?

2. Which square is the diving pool in?

3. Where should you go to watch archery?

4. Which sport is directly below the gymnastics arena?

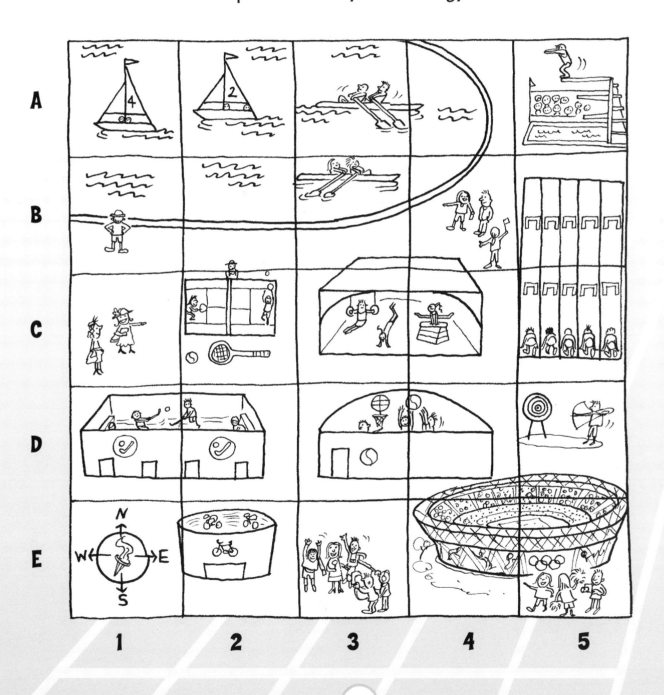

JET SETTERS

How many words of three letters or more can you create from the letters below? Two are listed to help you get started.

AROUND THE WORLD

1. HEART

2. TOWER

3. ___

4. ___

5. ___

6. ___

7. ___

8. ___

9. ___

10. ___

11. ___

12. ___

MAGICAL MARVIN

Help the magician find his rabbit by counting in threes, starting at the number 3.

RIDE 'EM COWBOY!

Yeehaw! Which of the silhouettes exactly matches the main picture?

FOODOKU

Solve the puzzle so that every row, column,
and mini-grid contains each of the four foods.

FLOWER FAIRIES

There are six things in the top picture that are not in the bottom picture. Can you circle them all?

SPY SCHOOL

Use the coded alphabet to find out where the spy is going on his next rendezvous.

SEA LIFE SQUARES

Cross out any letter that appears twice in a single grid. The letters you have left will spell the names of two sea creatures.

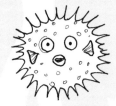
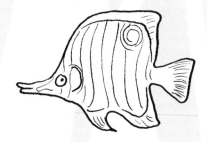

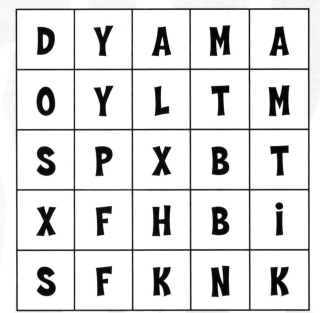

A	L	A	G	O
F	F	B	G	D
S	H	Q	H	M
C	T	N	E	D
N	C	Q	R	M

D	Y	A	M	A
O	Y	L	T	M
S	P	X	B	T
X	F	H	B	i
S	F	K	N	K

CRAZY CRABS

Find a route through the crazy crabs, following them in this order all the way through.

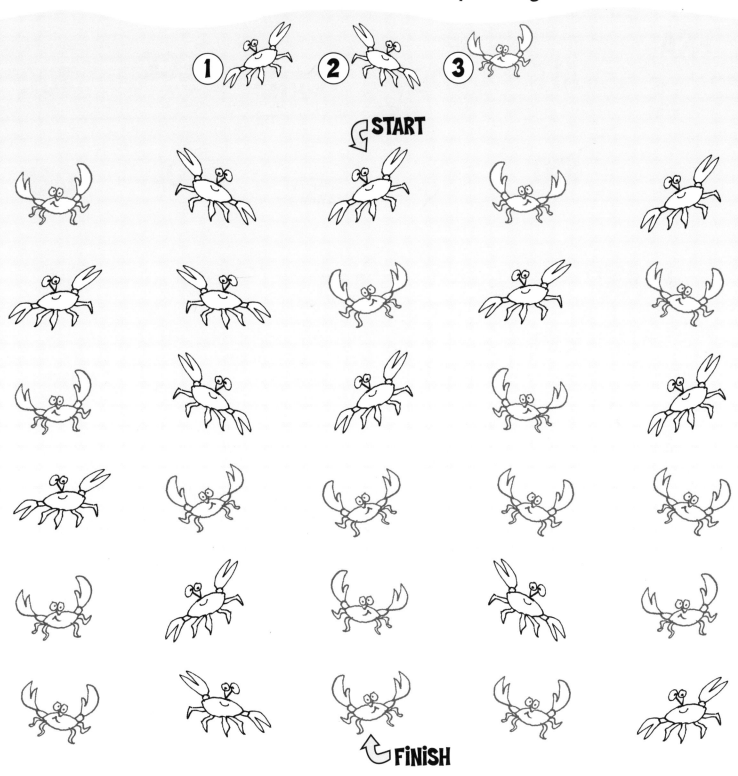

MAP MIX-UP

Match the boxes in pairs to make the names of ten different countries.
One has been done to help you get started.

FRA

AIT   DEN   CAN   ECE   TUR

ICO   SIA   KEY   POL   GRE

AND   NCE   ADA   ISR   SWE

MEX   KUW   AEL   RUS

| M | E | X | i | C | O |
| S | w | e | D | e | n |

| C | a | n | a | D | a |
| I | s | R | A | e | l |

| T | u | r | k | e | y |
| K | u | w | a | i | T |

| P | o | l | a | n | d |
| R | u | s | s | a | ? |

| G | r | e | e | c | e |
| F | r | a | n | c | e |

MONSTER TRUCK

Which jigsaw piece finishes the picture: a, b, c, d, or e?

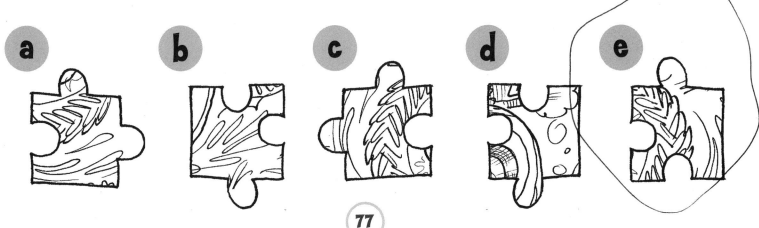

TAKING A TRIP

Help Jamie figure out how much his trip abroad is going to cost.

Jamie wants to fly to the Costa Lotta with his parents. How much will this be?

How much extra will it cost for four suitcases?

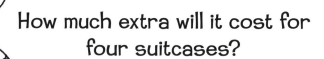

$100

At the Costa Lotta, they can catch the train to the Cathedral City. How much for three tickets?

One day, they rent a car to go to Splashworld theme park. How much is the car?

$60

$40

At Splashworld, they rent two towels and two umbrellas. How much do they spend?

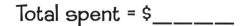

$5

Total spent = $_____

WHAT TO WEAR?

Which T-shirt does Emily want to wear today?
Use the clues to help her choose.

1. She doesn't want a plain one.
2. She's not in the mood for stripes.
3. She wants one with a white background.
4. She doesn't want one with a star on it.

CLIMBING THE WALL

Help Josh make his way up the climbing wall, using multiples of nine. Don't take a wrong turn!

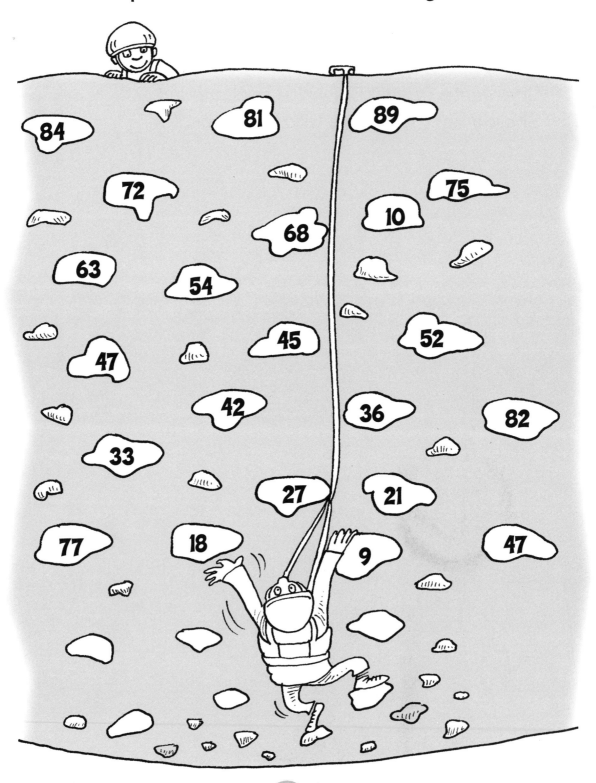

TIDY UP TIME

Simon Sprout the gardener has been raking leaves. How many can you count in the pile? How many hidden bugs can you count?

SPOT THE DIFFERENCE

There are six differences between these two pictures.
Can you circle them all?

SUDOKU

Solve the puzzle so that every row, column, and mini-grid contains the numbers 1 to 6.

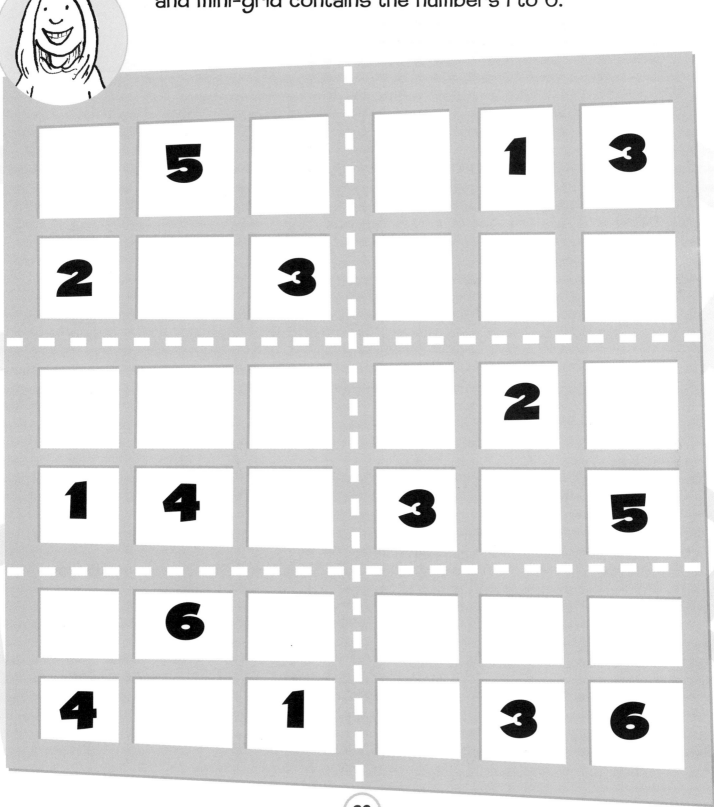

COOL CALCULATIONS

Figure out how much it costs to buy all the tasty treats in the circle.

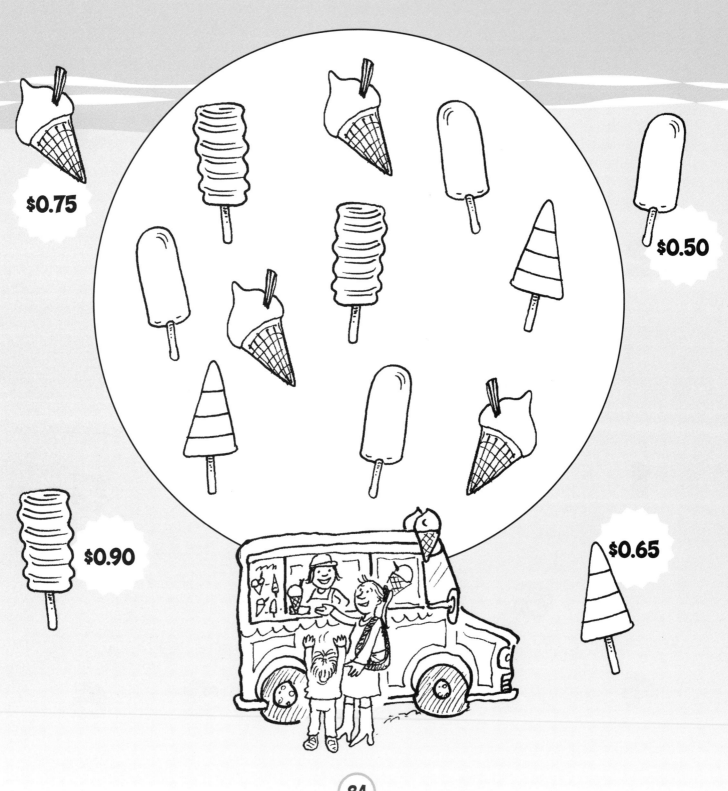

$0.75

$0.50

$0.90

$0.65

IN THE LAB

Look at the main picture of a science class, and then figure out which of the smaller pictures is the view of the class you would have from above.

TROPICAL PARADISE

Use your eagle eyes to spot each of the items listed at the bottom that are hidden in the main picture.

Find these:

SPY SCHOOL

Can you crack the code to find the joke?

WHAT DID THE SPY SAY WHEN HE GOT STUCK IN SEAWEED?

"KELP! KELP!"

OUT OF ORDER

Can you rearrange the six pictures so that they tell
the story in the correct order?

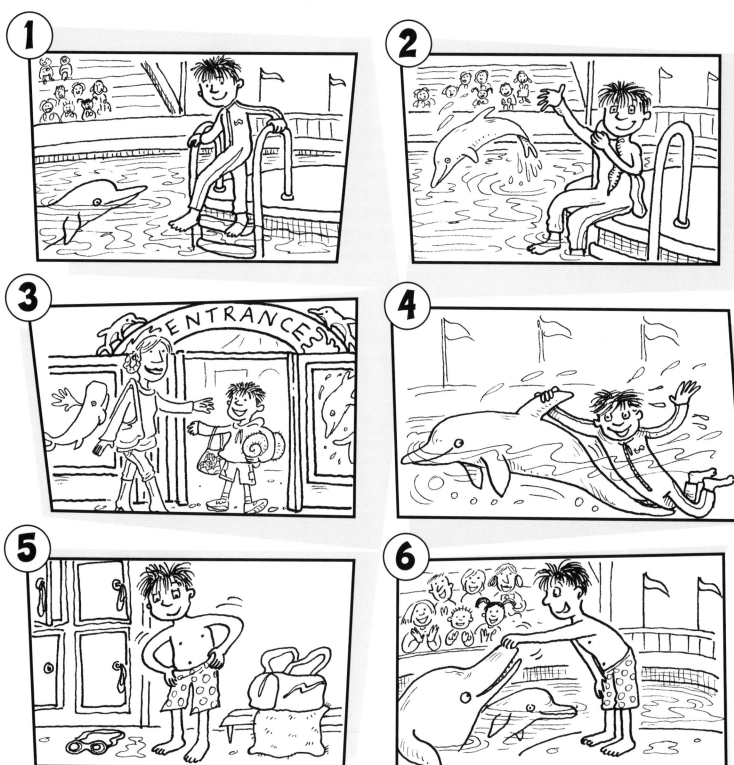

GRIDLOCKED

The mini-grid only appears once in the larger grid below.
Can you find it?

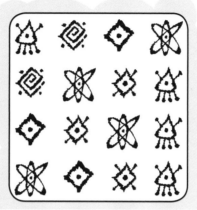

JEWEL THIEF

Answer the questions to fill in the code and help
the spy find the stolen jewels!

1. How many jewels are on the vase?

2. How many bags of money can you count?

3. How many gold bars are in the biggest pile?

4. How many necklaces are there altogether?

FLYING FUN

Put your memory to the test by studying this picture for three minutes. Then turn the page to see how many questions you can answer correctly.

AIR SHOW THIS SATURDAY

HOT DOGS

88

FLYING FUN

How much can you remember about the picture on the previous page?

1. How many planes are flying in the diamond formation?

2. Is the helicopter in the air or on the ground?

3. How many flags are at the entrance?

4. How many parachutes can you count?

5. What pattern is on the lady's knitted hat?

6. What two types of food are on sale?

7. How many long trails of smoke can you count?

8. What day is it?

9. What number is on the helicopter?

10. How many people are using binoculars?

DELICIOUS DESSERTS

Only two of these ice-cream sundaes are exactly the same.
Can you spot them?

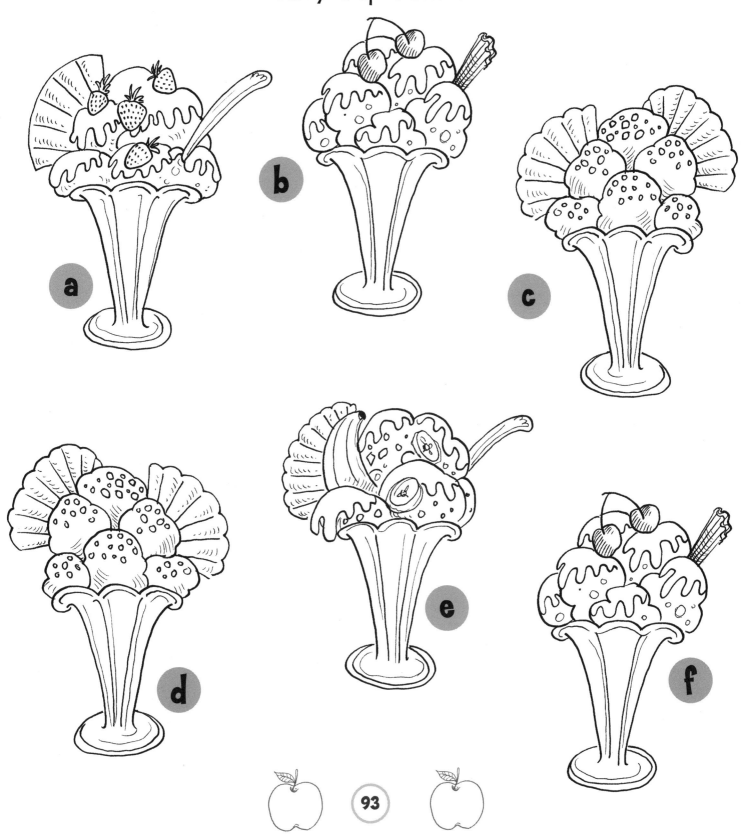

BUGOKU

Solve the puzzle so that every row, column, and
mini-grid contains each of the four bugs.

TREASURE HUNT

Follow the directions to find out where the ancient treasure is buried.

1. Start in square E5 by the babbling brook.
2. Walk two squares west past the castle.
3. Head north two squares to the ancient church.
4. Turn west in the direction of the burial mound and walk for one square.
5. Head north one square. Put an X to mark the treasure!

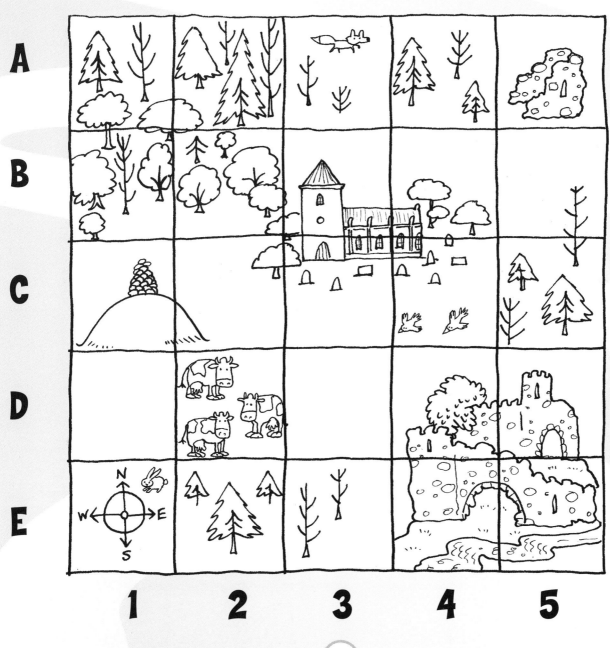

CREEPY CRAWLIES

Unscramble the words using the letters in each section.
Each answer is something that flies, scuttles, or stings!

L B E
M B
E B U

T B
L E
E E

T E I
D E P
N C E

T F U
L
B E T
Y R

FIRE DRILL

Help the fire engine join the firemen at the practice
building by counting in fours.

START

| 4 | 8 | 12 | 16 |
| 72 | 68 | 64 | 20 |

116	112	100	96	76	80	60	24
120	108	104	92	88	84	56	28
124	128					52	32
136	132					48	36
140						44	40

FINISH

LIBRARY CODES

This spy has been sent to the library to pick up his next message. Use the code to figure out which section he must visit.

A	✿
B	✲
C	✳
D	❄
E	❅
F	❆
G	✴
H	✸
I	✺
J	✹
K	✳
L	●
M	○
N	■
O	◻
P	◻
Q	◻
R	◻
S	▲
T	▼
U	◆
V	❖
W	◗
X	✷
Y	✸
Z	✺

PLAY TIME

Can you spot which five items are missing in the bottom picture?

ALPHADOKU

Solve the puzzle so that every row, column,
and mini-grid contains each of the letters A to F.

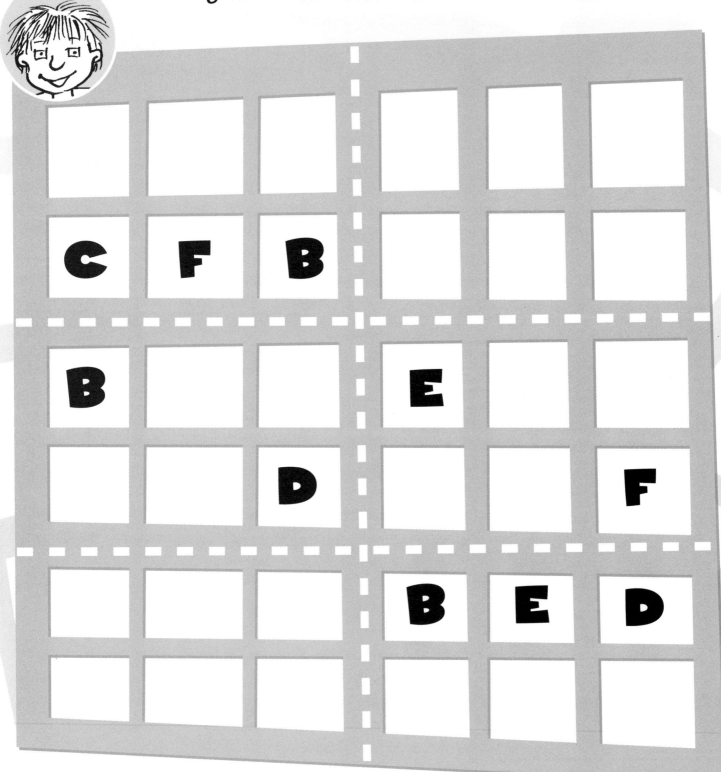

TOTALLY TROPICAL

How many tropical fish can you count on this page?

PARTY BAGS

Annika is having a birthday party. Can you help her add up how much money she could spend on her party bags?

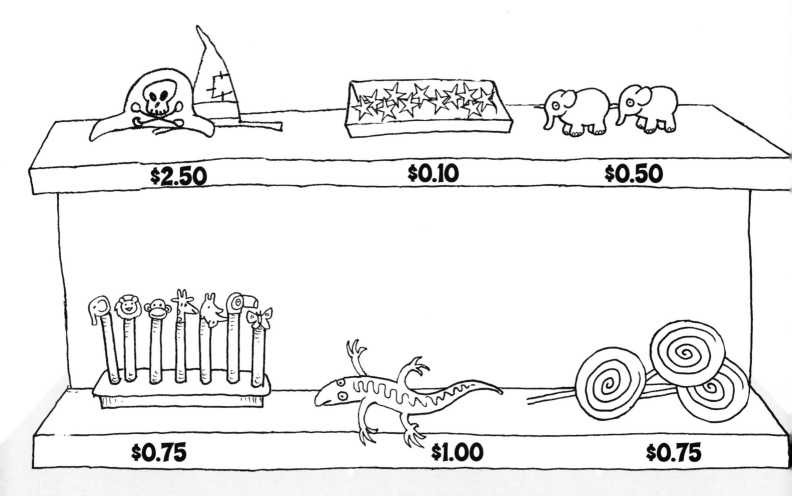

$2.50 $0.10 $0.50

$0.75 $1.00 $0.75

1. How much will a party bag cost if it contains a toy lizard, two stars, and an elephant?

2. What will it cost to give each guest a hat, a lollipop, and a pencil?

3. What will a party bag cost if it contains one of each item?

FANTASTIC GYMNASTICS

Look at the people in this gym class. They've moved around a lot between pictures! Can you find two new people and the two people who left?

SUMMER OLYMPICS

Can you find these ten Summer Olympic events in the grid?
Look for the names hidden across, down, or diagonally.

ARCHERY   **FENCING**

ATHLETICS   **HANDBALL**

BADMINTON   **ROWING**

BOXING   **SWIMMING**

DIVING   **TENNIS**

F	i	B	O	F	E	N	C	i	N	G	C
E	A	H	A	N	D	B	A	L	L	F	R
N	T	X	R	D	G	G	O	i	W	S	O
M	H	S	C	i	M	N	R	X	i	A	W
i	L	W	H	V	B	i	U	N	i	R	i
N	E	i	E	i	O	H	N	A	B	N	N
G	T	M	R	N	X	E	B	T	H	O	G
B	i	T	Y	G	T	A	O	H	O	A	X
O	C	E	A	S	W	i	M	M	i	N	G
X	S	i	N	G	H	A	N	D	F	Y	Y

WHAT NEXT?

Study the sequence of pictures carefully and figure out which statue finishes the pattern: a, b, or c?

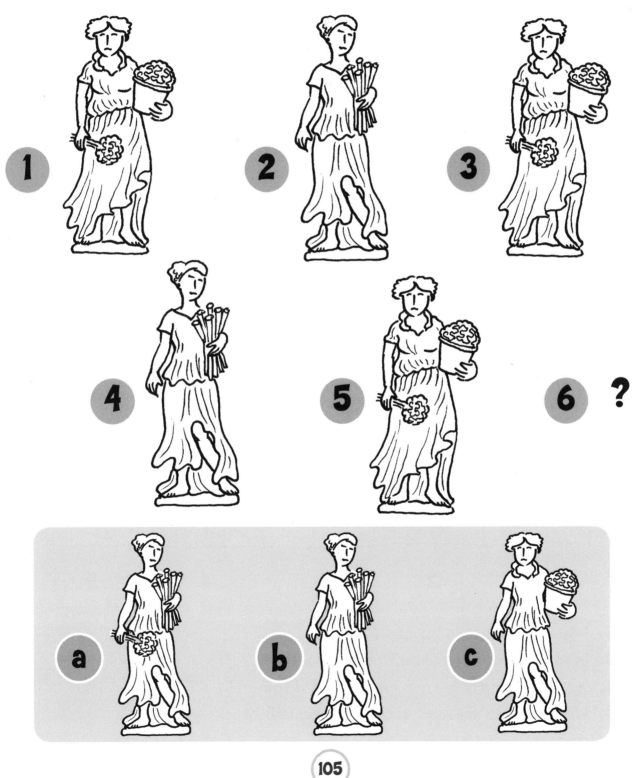

CASTLE CAPERS

Answer the questions with the grid references from the map.

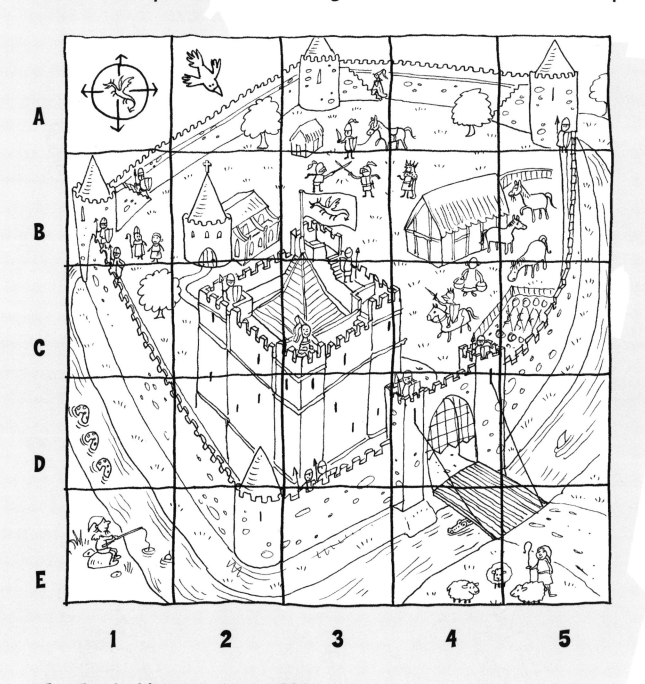

1. What building is in square B2?
2. In which square can you find the portcullis?
3. Which square does not have a guard tower: B1, E3, A5, or A3?
4. What animals are kept in the building in B4?

SPY SCHOOL

Can you figure out what this message says?

CHILL-OUT TIME

Can you guide the girl through the maze
to reach her towel on the beach?

START

FINISH

BIRD BRAINS

Match the boxes in pairs to make the names of ten different birds.
One has been done to help you get started.

TOU   PUF   PAR   KEY   EON

KOO   TUR   THR   PIG   FAL

MAG   FIN   CON   ROT   CON

DOR   USH   PIE   CUC   CAN

T	O	U	C	A	N

SPOT THE DIFFERENCE

There are six things in the top picture that do not appear in the bottom picture. Can you circle them all?

FOODOKU

Solve the sudoku puzzle so that every row, column, and mini-grid contains each of the four foods.

RAINY-DAY PUZZLE

How many words of three letters or more can you create from the letters below? Two are listed to help you get started.

RAINING CATS AND DOGS

1   STRONG   7 _____

2   GROSS   8 _____

3 _____   9 _____

4 _____   10 _____

5 _____   11 _____

6 _____   12 _____

FAIRY TALE

Which jigsaw piece finishes the picture: a, b, c, d, or e?

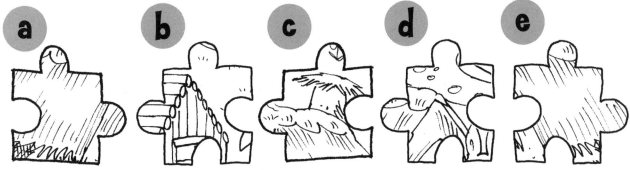

a   b   c   d   e

NUMBER CRUNCH

Figure out which number is represented by each symbol to make the equations add up in every row and column.

DINO CLUB

This spiny dinosaur is on the prowl! But which silhouette matches him exactly?

POP PUZZLER

Find a route through the lollipops, following them in this order all the way through.

① ② ③

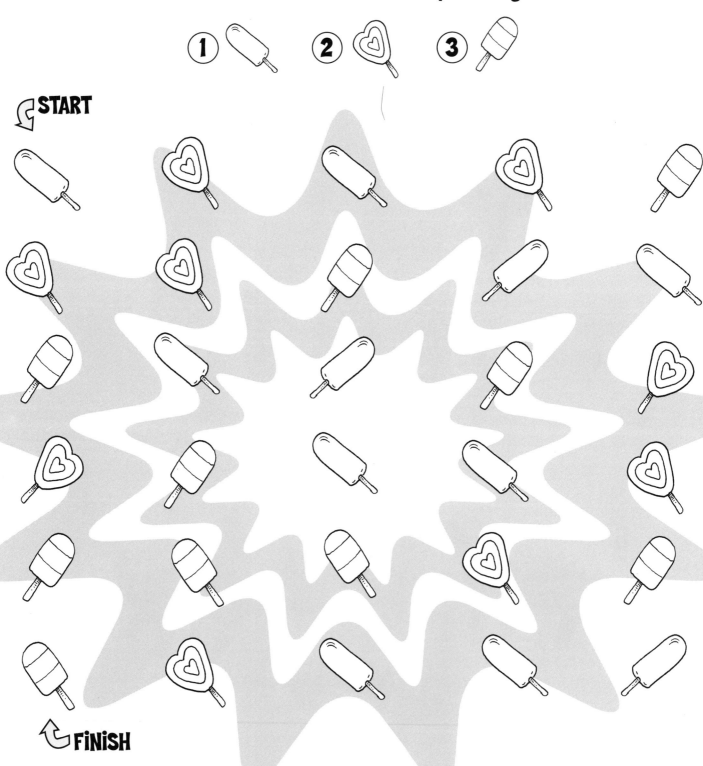

START

FINISH

OCTOPLUS

Solve each of the addition problems held by the octopus to fill in the code and unlock the treasure chest.

$5\frac{1}{4} + 2\frac{3}{4} =$

$3\frac{1}{3} + 1\frac{2}{3} =$

$1\frac{1}{2} + 4\frac{1}{2} =$

$\frac{3}{4} + 1\frac{1}{4} =$

Enter code here

TREASURE HUNT

Follow the directions and put an X where the pirate treasure is buried.

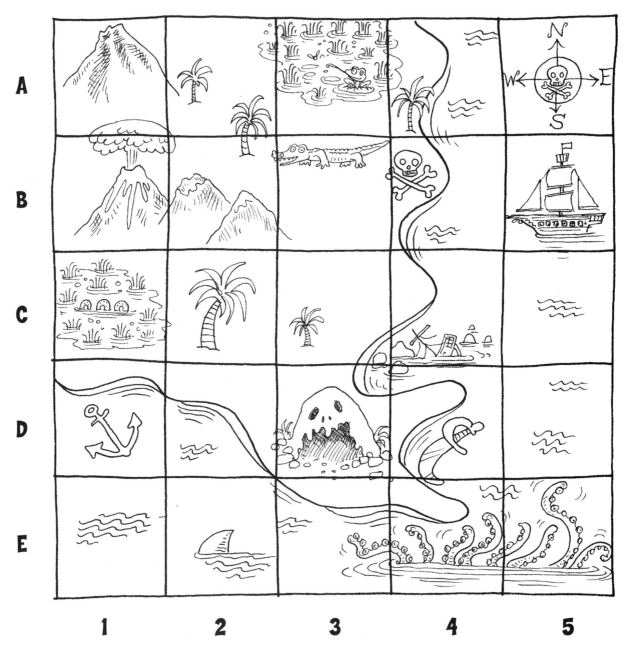

1. Set sail to Cutlass Cove in square D4.
2. Proceed on foot to Skull Cave in square D3.
3. Head due north three squares to the swamplands. Be careful not to sink!
4. Walk two squares west and one square south and start to dig!

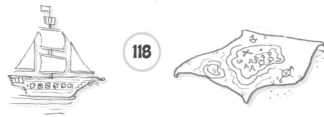

SPY SCHOOL

Can you figure out what this message says?

WHAT DO YOU CALL A SPY WHO HIDES AT THE BEACH?

SANDY!

IN A TWIRL

Fill in the missing numbers on the gymnast's ribbon with multiples of eight.

BEAUTIFUL BUTTERFLIES

Which of these butterflies is the odd one out?

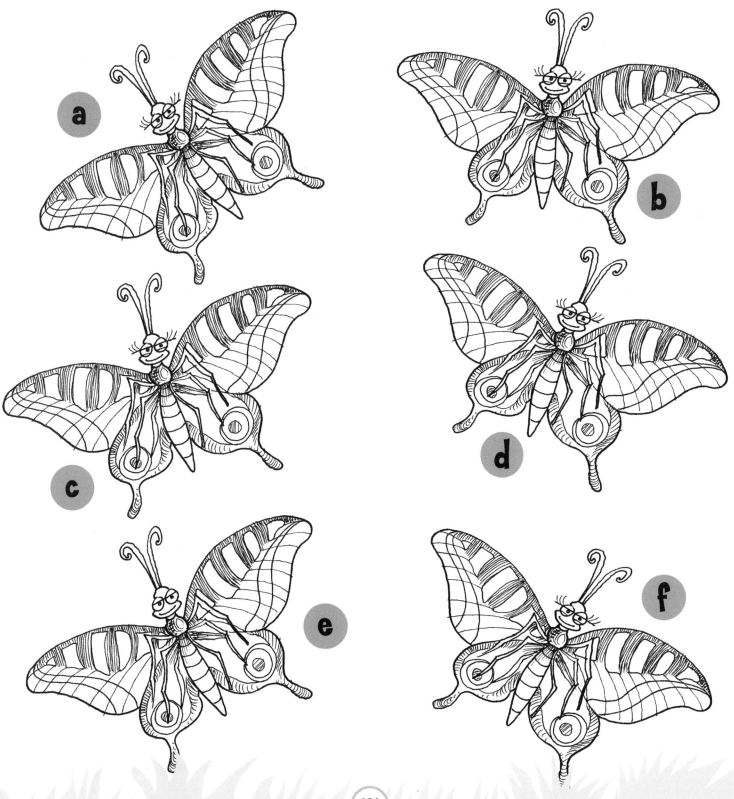

SUDOKU

Solve the puzzle so that each row, column,
and mini-grid contains the numbers 1 to 6.

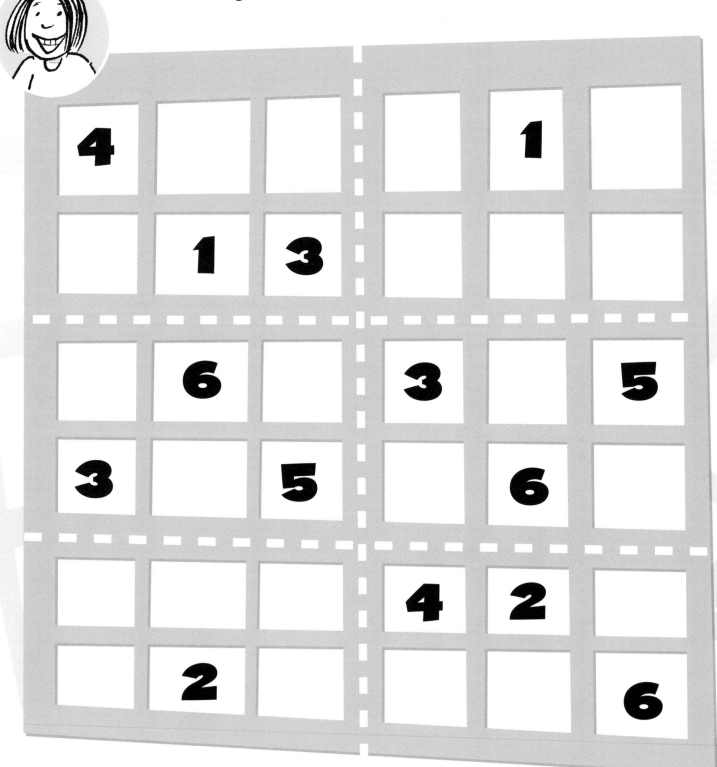

FAST FOOD FRAZZLER

Put your memory to the test by studying this picture for three minutes. Then turn the page to see how many questions you can answer correctly.

FAST FOOD FRAZZLER

How much can you remember about the picture
on the previous page?

1. How many baseball hats can you see?

2. Who is pushing the baby in a stroller - a man or a woman?

3. What does the little girl have on her backpack?

4. What two foods are on the menu on the table?

5. How many people are sitting at the table?

6. Is the server at the counter a man or a woman?

7. How many straws are in the drink on the table?

8. How many potted plants can you see?

9. What toy is the little boy holding?

10. How many people are wearing glasses?

GRIDLOCKED

The mini-grid only appears once in the larger grid below.
Can you find it?

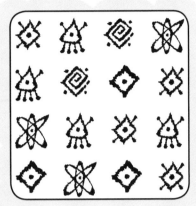

FIRE STARTERS

Only two of these dragons are exactly the same.
Can you spot which two?

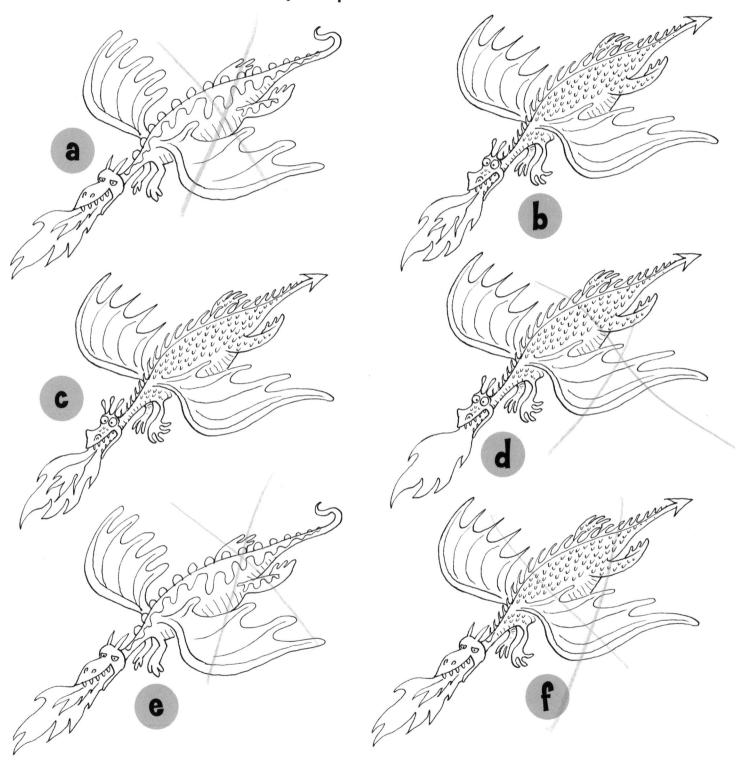

OUT OF ORDER

Can you rearrange the six pictures so that they tell the story in the correct order?

SHOPPING TRIP

Answer the questions with the grid references from the map.

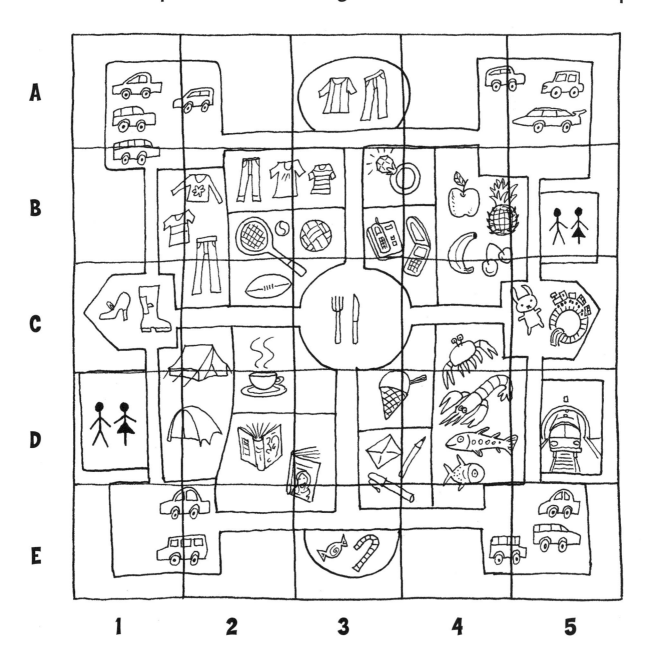

	1	2	3	4	5
A					
B					
C					
D					
E					

1. Which square is not suitable for parking your car: A1, E1, D1, or E5?
2. In which square can you buy shoes?
3. What kind of store is in A3?
4. Which square would you visit to buy chocolate?

SNAIL TRAIL

Can you fit each of the creepy crawlies from the list into the spaces on the snail shell? The shaded spaces show the last letter of one word and the first letter of the next.

GLOWWORM

HORNET

TERMITE

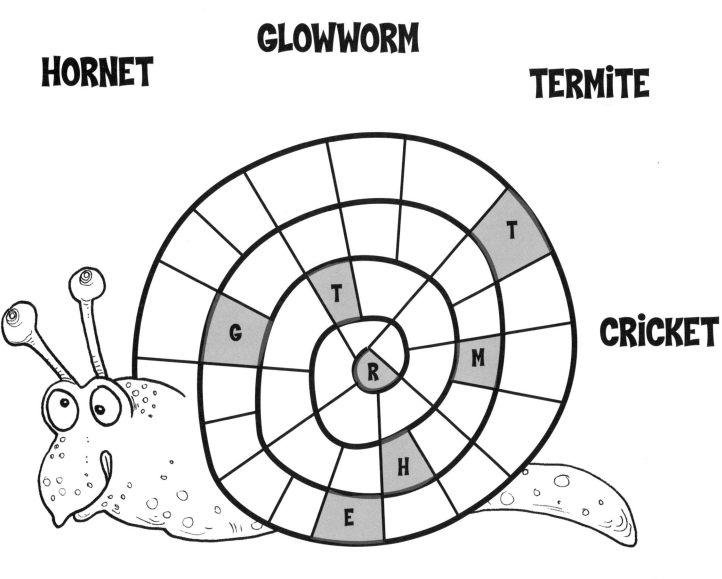

CRICKET

MOTH

EARWIG

TREEHOPPER

ROLL THE DICE

Use the numbers from the dice to finish the equations.

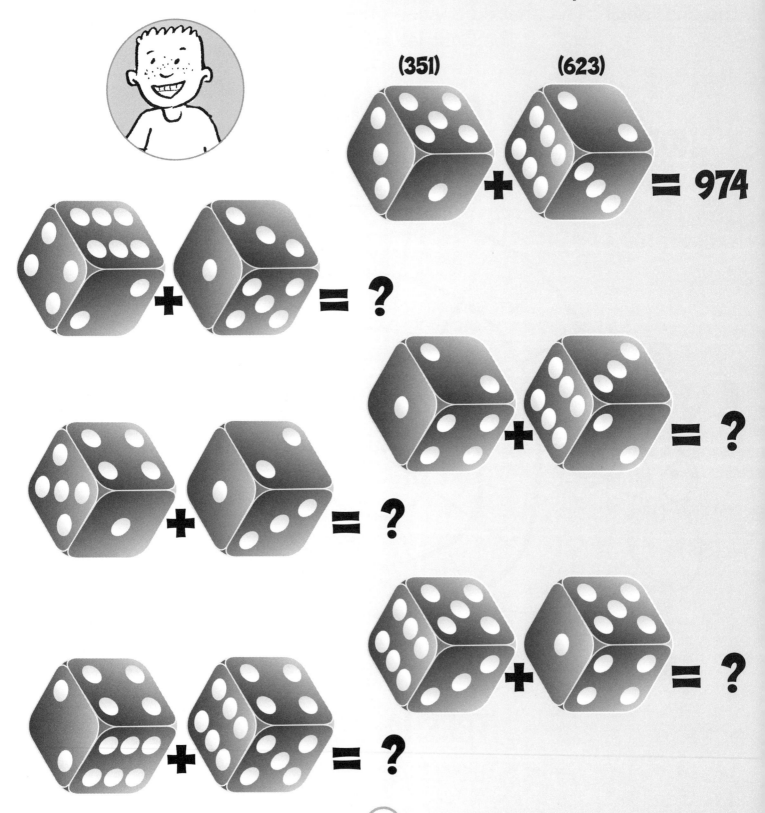

(351)   (623)

+ = 974

JUNGLE FEVER

Use the coded alphabet to find out which part of the
tropical house the spy must visit to meet her contact.

CIRCUS SEVENS

Find your way from the trapeze artist to the ringmaster by counting in sevens, starting at the number 7. Are you ready for a challenge?

	1	17	12	28	35	42
		11	16	21	25	49
			START 7	14	33	56
37		41	44	52	50	63
FINISH 105	98	91	84	77	70	
		96	90	79	75	
		100	95	83	88	

WITCH NEXT?

Study the sequence of pictures carefully and figure out which witch finishes the pattern: a, b, or c?

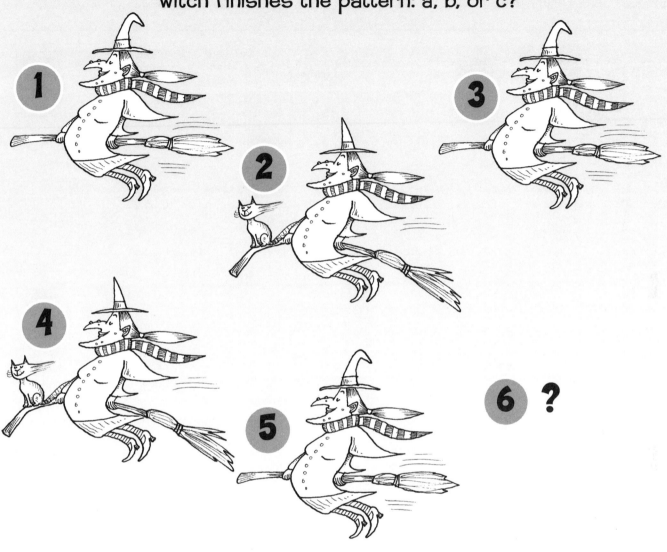

SPOT THE DIFFERENCE

There are six things in the top picture that do not appear in the bottom picture. Can you circle them?

NUMBER CRUNCH

Figure out which number is represented by each symbol to make the equations add up in every row and column.

CAMPING TRIP

Change the word HIKE to the word CAMP one letter at a time.
The arrows show you which letter to change each time.
Make sure you create a real word with every change.

H I K E

C A M P

GHASTLY GHOSTS

How many ghosts are haunting this page? How many bats are fluttering among them?

PARTY PUZZLE

Use your eagle eyes to spot each of the things listed on the left that are hidden in the main picture.

Find these!

PAINTER'S PALETTE

In each section, cross out any letter that appears twice.
The remaining letters spell out three paints that the artist is using.

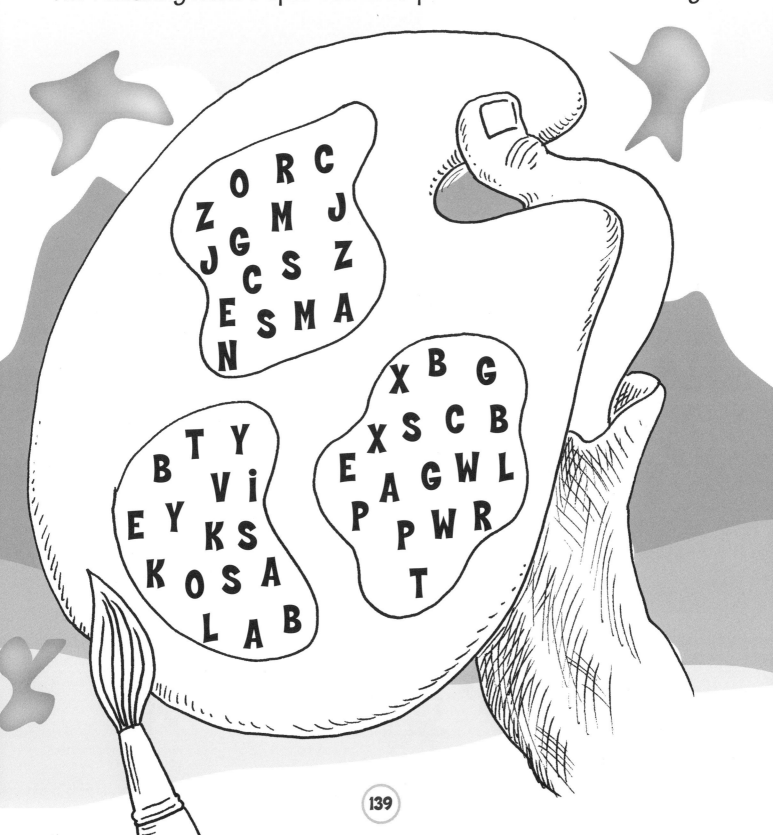

ALL CHANGE

This chameleon is eyeing up his lunch! Which of the silhouettes exactly matches the main picture?

FLYING FARTHEST

Add up the numbers on each jet trail to see which plane has flown the farthest.

26   20   4   18

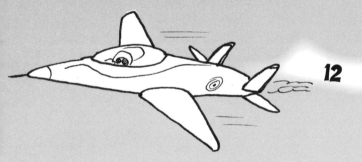

12   12   6   25

30   15   9   5

FOODOKU

Solve the puzzle so that every row, column, and mini-grid contains each of the four foods.

TRACK SIDE

Can you spot which five items are different in the right-hand picture?

HIDDEN GNOMES

How many times can you find the word GNOME in the grid?
It only appears across, down, and forward - not backward.

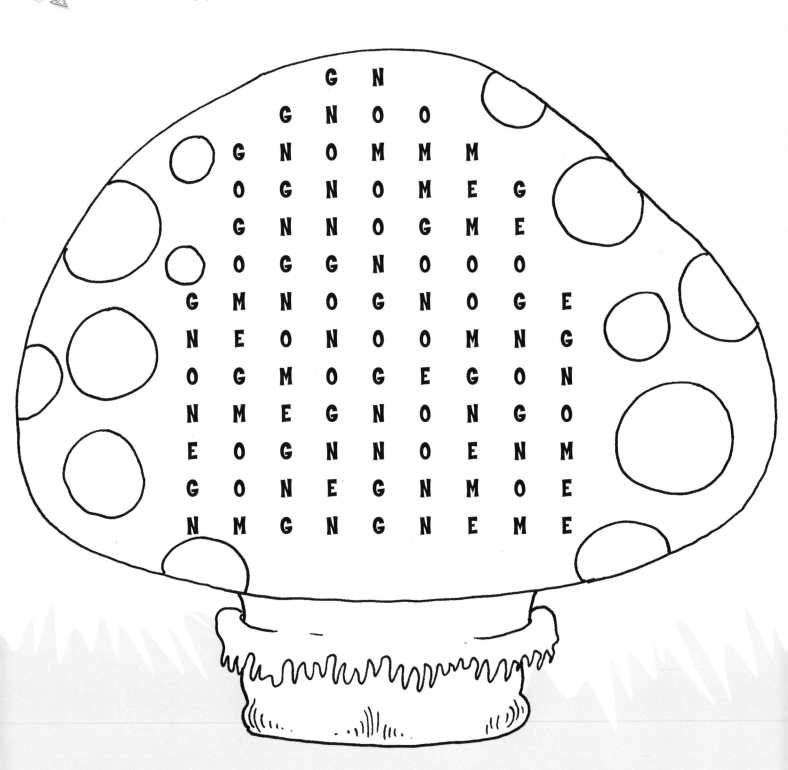

```
      G   N
  G   N   O   O
G   N   O   M   M   M
O   G   N   O   M   E   G
G   N   N   O   G   M   E
O   G   G   N   O   O   O
G   M   N   O   G   N   O   G   E
N   E   O   N   O   O   M   N   G
O   G   M   O   G   E   G   O   N
N   M   E   G   N   O   N   G   O
E   O   G   N   N   O   E   N   M
G   O   N   E   G   N   M   O   E
N   M   G   N   G   N   E   M   E
```

TEEPEE TEASER

Which of these teepees is described below?

1. It's decorated with zigzags.
2. It doesn't have spots.
3. There are no bird pictures on it.
4. There are triangles around the bottom.

FARMER BEN'S HEN

Help Farmer Ben drive his tractor through the maze to find his lost hen.

EATEN EIGHTS

How many apples has this worm eaten? He's only guilty
of munching those that can be divided by 8.

8

27

21

18

56

35

42

24

80

48

70

32

38

96

72

40

81

16

28

64

JUNGLE TREASURE

Follow the directions and draw an X where the treasure is buried.

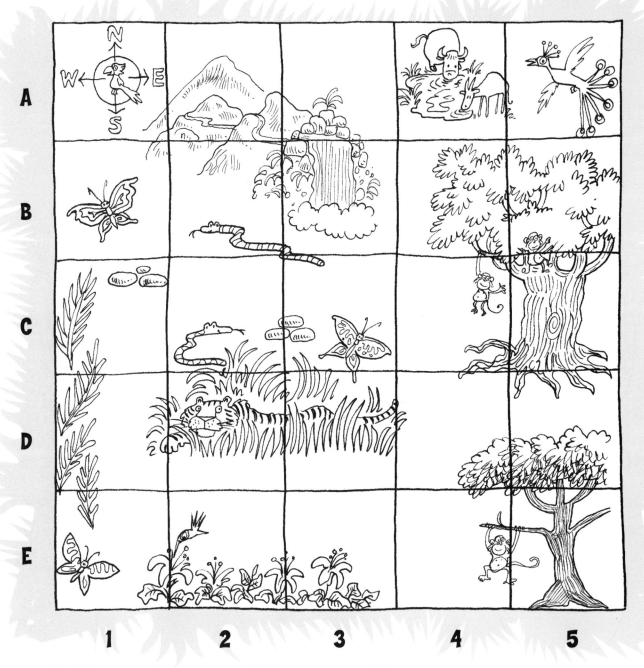

1. Start at the watering hole in square A4.
2. Head south past the waterfall for two squares.
3. Stride west from the roots of the giant tangle tree for three squares.
4. Walk two squares south to avoid the tiger, and then two squares east.

BUGOKU

Solve the puzzle so that every row, column, and mini-grid contains each of the four bugs.

BEAT THE TEACHER

The teacher can't figure out the answer to this problem.
Which of the clever students is correct?

OUTDOOR FUN

Look at the main picture of Charlie outdoors, and then figure out which of the smaller pictures is the view you would have from above.

a **b** **c**

d **e** **f**

PET CITY

Can you find ten popular pets hiding in the grid?
They might be written across, down, diagonally, backward, or forward.

**MOUSE   SNAKE   PARROT   RABBIT   DOG
CAT   GERBIL   LIZARD   HAMSTER   GOLDFISH**

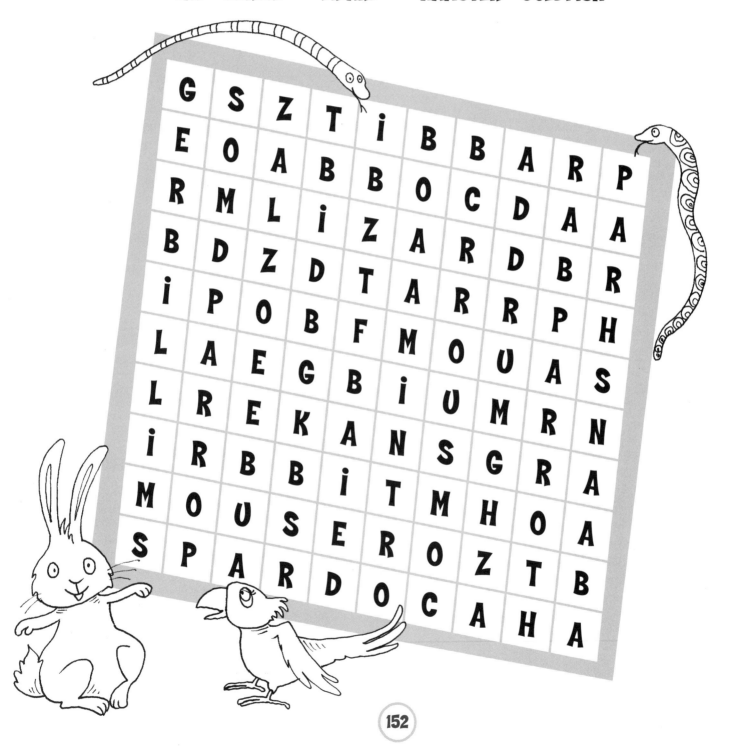

FANCY THAT!

Look at the people in their fancy costumes. They have all moved around between pictures! Can you find two new people and the two who left?

TROPHY CABINET

Find your way through the trophies, following them in this order all the way through.

JURASSIC PARK

How many words of three letters or more can you create from the letters below? Two words are listed to help you get started.

DIPLODOCUS

1 CLOUD

2 SOIL

3

4

5

6

7

8

9

10

11

12

SPY SCHOOL

Can you figure out what this message says?

WHY DID THE SILLY SPY GO TO NIGHT SCHOOL?

HE WANTED TO LEARN TO READ IN THE DARK.

AT THE BALLET

Only two of these pairs of ballet dancers are exactly the same.
Can you spot them?

SKI RUN

Fill in the missing numbers. Add 11 each time you go under a flag.

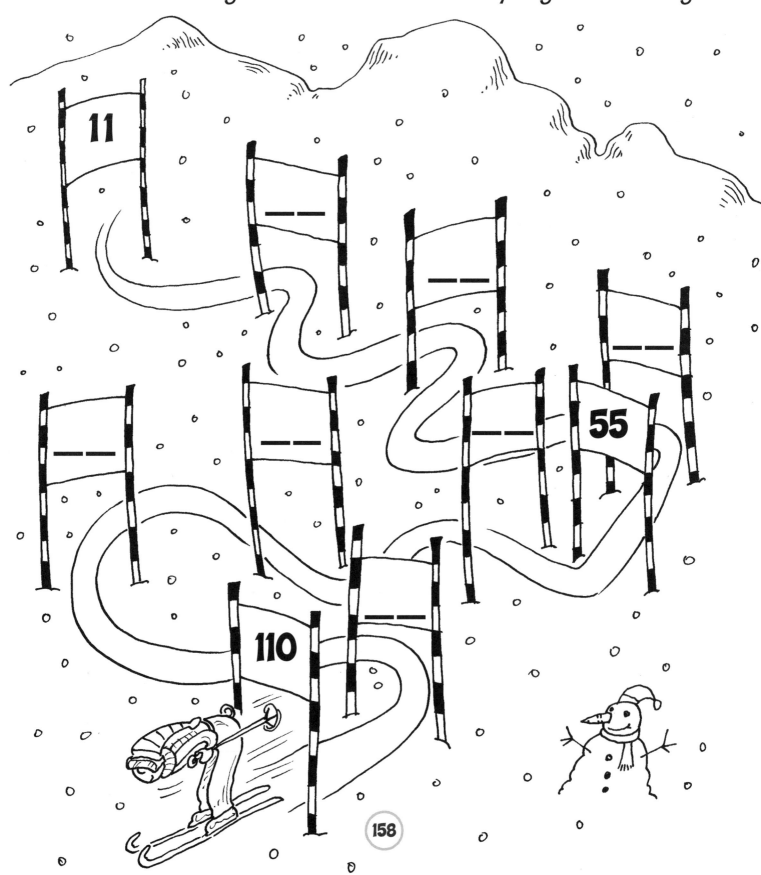

11

55

110

158

WALKING THE DOG

Trudi is walking her dogs - or is it the other way around?
See if you can spot 10 differences between these two pictures.

GREEK ODYSSEY

Help Sophia through the Greek ruins to find her family.
Watch out for the sneaky snakes!

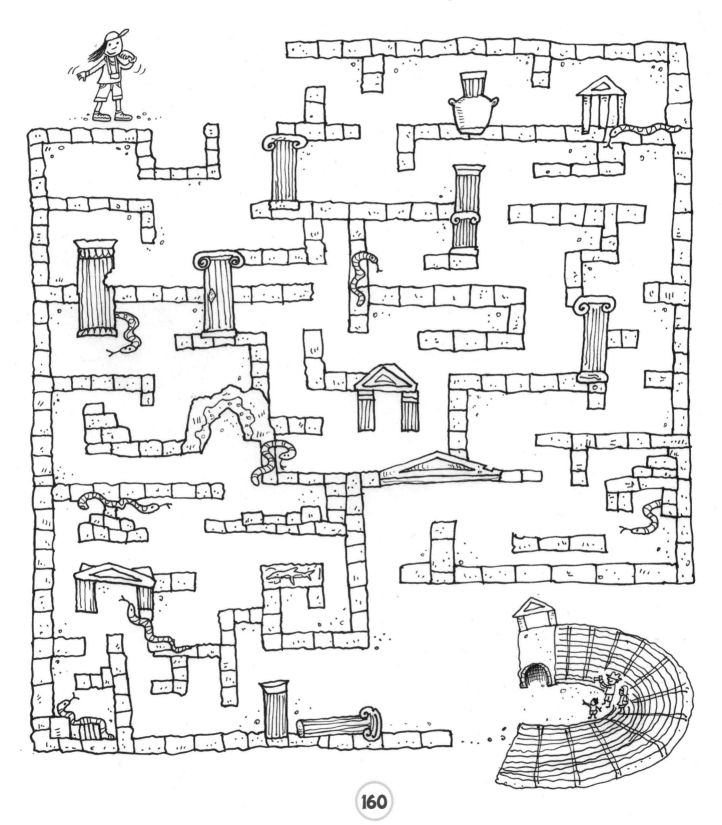

COWBOY CRACKER

Use the code to find out the answer
to this silly cowboy joke.

Why did the cowboy think his pony had a sore throat?

A D E G H i L O

N P R S T W Y

_ _ _ _ _ _

_ _ _ _ _ _ _   _ _ _ _ _ _ _

SLALOM SCORE

Add up the numbers on each canoe course to find out which boat was the quickest - the one with the lowest number.

SURPRISE!

The game warden has found some wildlife - but what wildlife has crept up behind him?

SIX PACK

Help Rocket Girl track down The Mighty Muscleman by finding a path, using numbers that appear in the six times table.

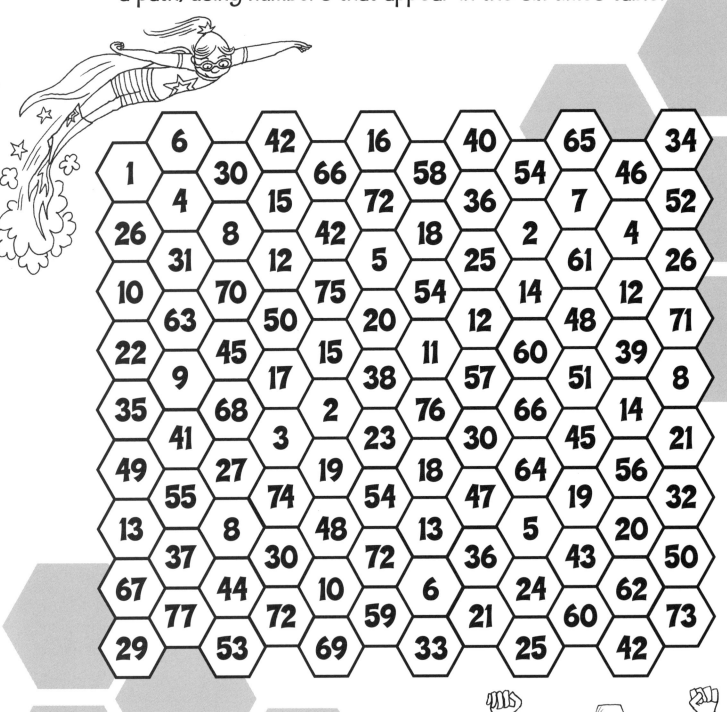

MOUSE TRAP

Can you find the missing mice? The word MOUSE appears in the grid three times. Search up, down, across, and diagonally.

```
M  O  S  U  E  E
O  U  S  E  M  U  S  E
U  M  O  M  O  U  S  E  M
U  O  M  M  O  U  S  M  O
M  U  U  M  O  O  S  E  U
O  O  O  O  M  O  S  M  S
U  M  O  U  S  E  M  O  S
   S  S  S  M  U  O  U  E
   E  E  S  O  U  S  M
         M  S  O  E
```

DESTINATION UNKNOWN

The ticket office at Totally Brilliant Airways is in an uproar! Can you match the torn tickets to name six capital cities?

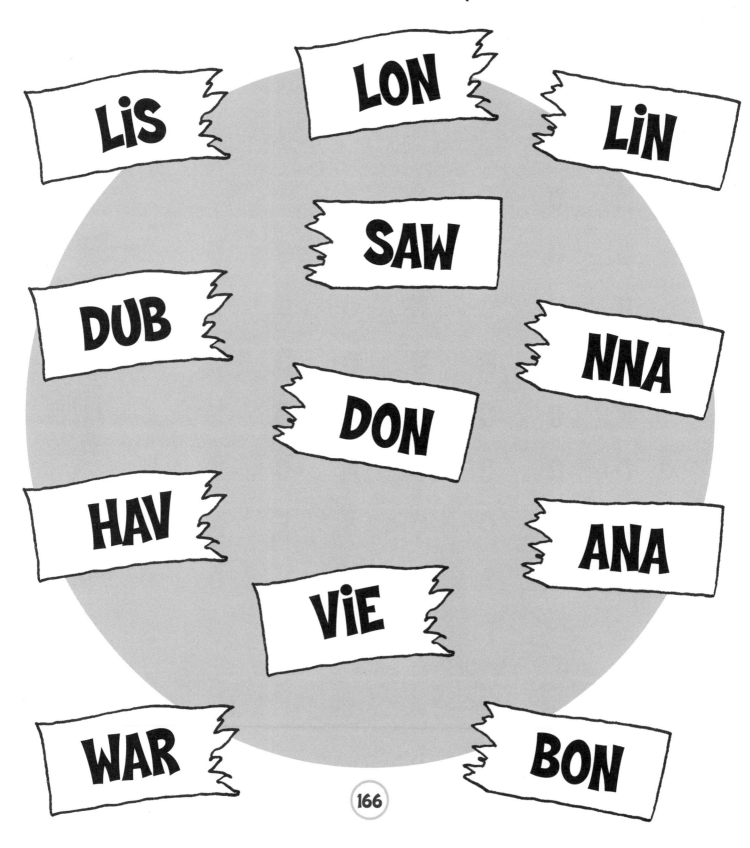

LIS

LON

LIN

SAW

DUB

NNA

DON

HAV

ANA

VIE

WAR

BON

RODEO RIDER

Which of the pieces finishes the jigsaw picture?

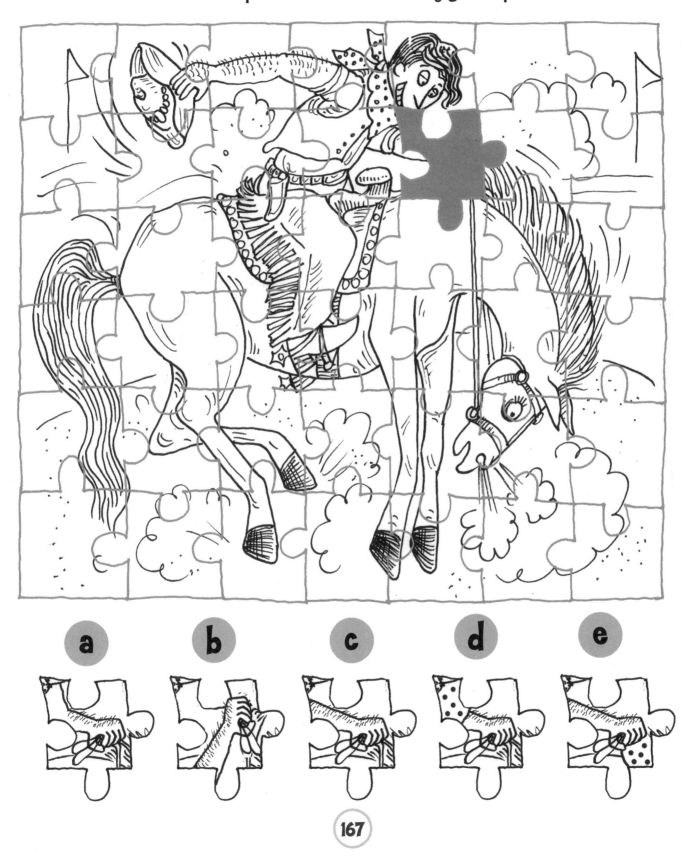

ON THE BALL

Use only the letters on balls you hit to spell out the name of a sport.
There is a clue on the page to help you.

A team sport with six players on each side and a net in the middle.

PENGUIN PARADE

Each of these penguins has an identical twin, except for one.
Who is it?

A PRICKLY PROBLEM

Which of the pictures needs to replace the question mark to correctly finish the pattern?

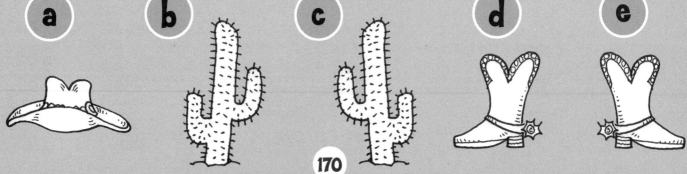

PLAY TIME

Hammy the hamster is bored. Can you draw some toys for him to play with?

TIME FOR A TRIP

Use the unusual clock to spell out two places that Johnny has visited. Follow the instructions carefully.

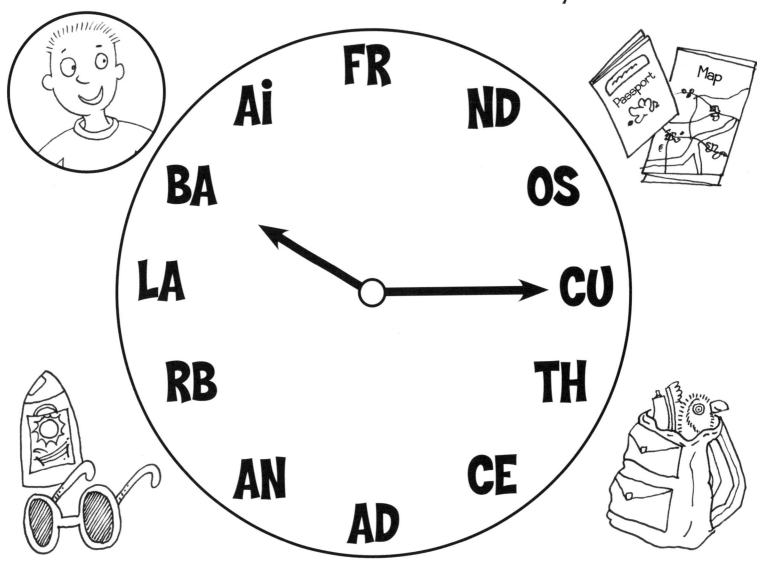

Write down the letters shown by the minute hand, then by the hour hand, for each time listed below. Together, they will spell the places you are looking for. For example, quarter past ten = CUBA.

a
twenty past eleven
quarter to one

b
ten to eight
half past two

CROSS-EYED

How many heart shapes can
you count in the picture below?

BULLSEYE

Add up the scores on each target to see who has scored the most points. Use the key to help you.

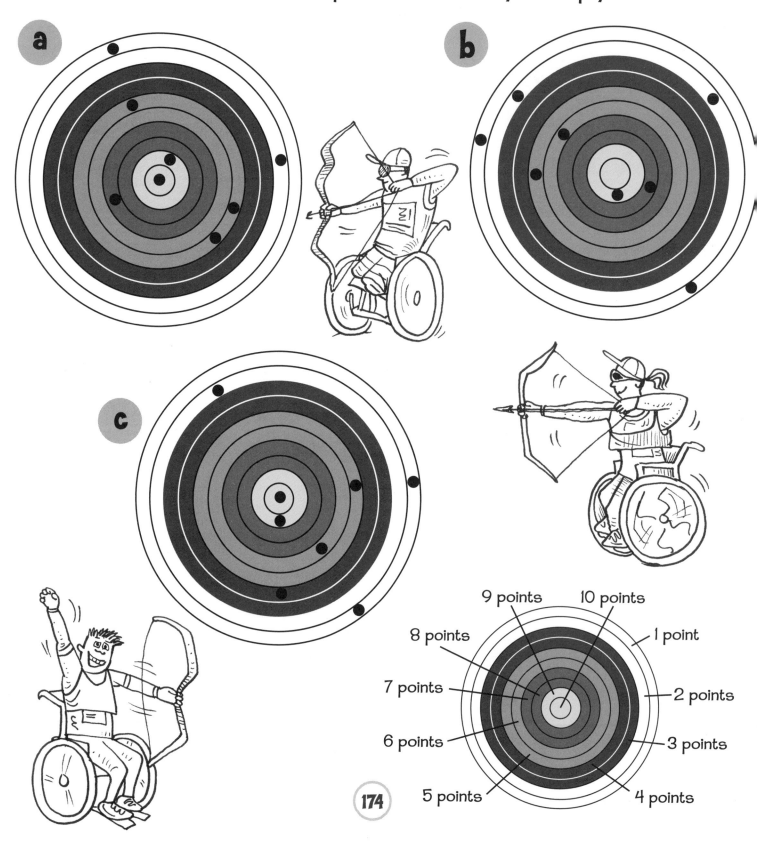

SUPERBAD

The Blue Comet is on the tail of another super villain! Shade every square containing the letters B, D, or M, and the remaining letters will spell the name of the evildoer who must be stopped!

B	D	B	D	M	M	M	B	D	M
M	B	D	D	M	B	B	M	B	D
M	K	B	R	A	D	B	L	L	M
D	D	M	B	D	M	D	M	D	M
B	M	D	B	D	M	M	B	B	D
M	T	B	D	H	B	D	M	D	M
B	D	M	B	D	E	M	B	D	M
C	O	B	D	N	M	B	Q	D	D
M	B	U	E	D	D	M	M	B	M
D	M	D	B	B	R	D	O	R	B

SETTING UP HOME

A badger's home is made up of underground tunnels and called a sett. In which order must Mrs. Badger travel through the tunnels to first collect sticks and then leaves, before taking them to her babies?

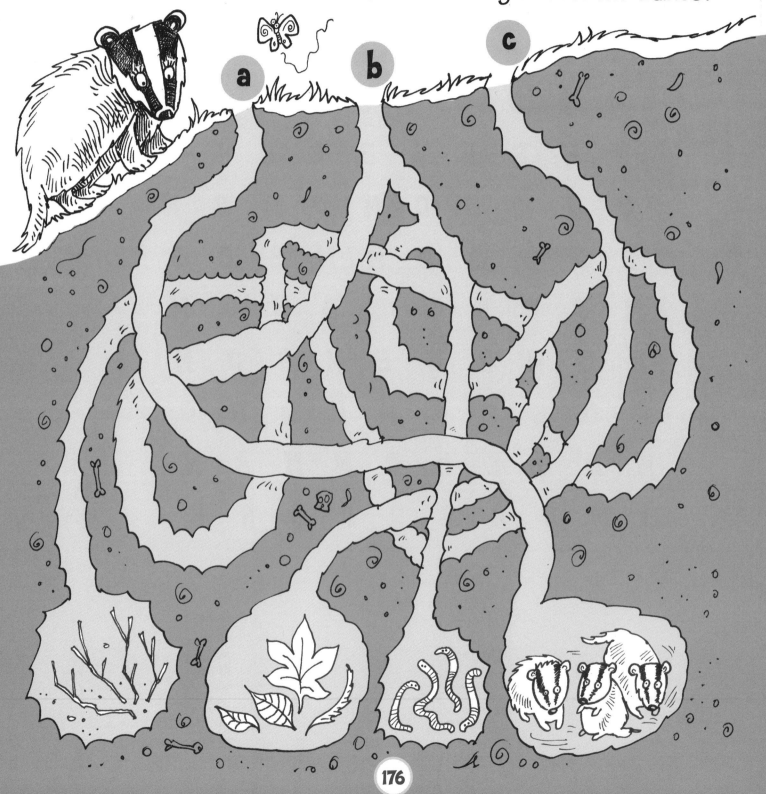

BEST IN SHOW

How many new words with three or more letters can you create from the letters below? One has been done to help you get started.

PETS WIN PRIZES

PRINT

1. _____
2. _____
3. _____
4. _____
5. _____
6. _____
7. _____
8. _____
9. _____
10. _____
11. _____
12. _____
13. _____
14. _____
15. _____

SWEET TREATS

Yummy! Katie is on summer break, and it's time for ice cream.
Find a path from the top of the grid to the bottom, following the ice
creams in the order shown.

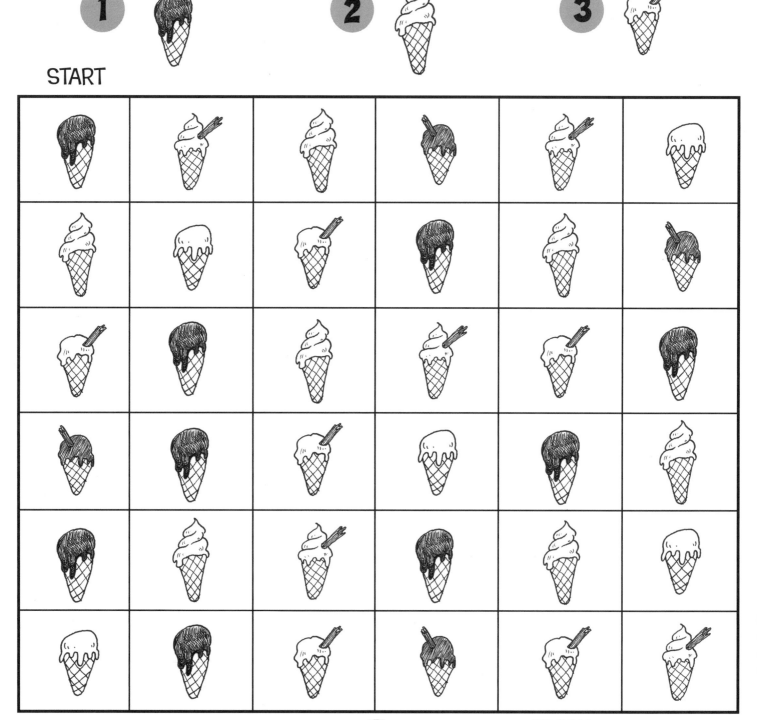

HATS OFF

Who do you think this hat belongs to? Cowgirl Cara or maybe Wild Jim McWestern? Draw the best cowboy or cowgirl you can imagine.

ALL-TIME GREATS

Cross out every other letter on each race track, starting at the numbered arrows. The answer in each lane will reveal the only five sports that have been in every summer Olympic games since 1896.

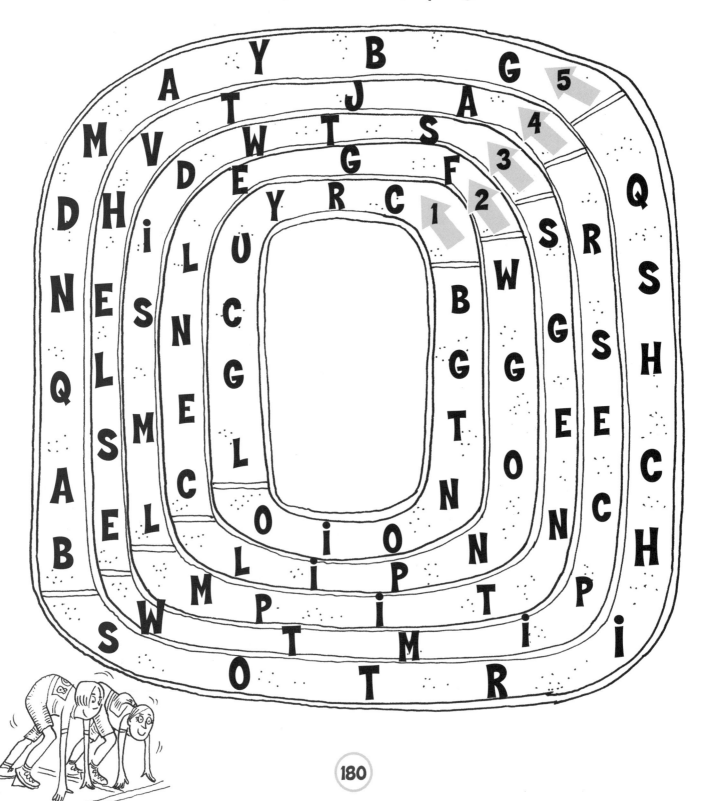

180

PERFECT PRIMATES

Primates are a group of animals that includes monkeys, apes, and humans.
Find all the listed primates, including Norman, the nutty human!

MANDRILL
MARMOSET
BABOON
CHIMP
GIBBON
AYE-AYE

MONKEY
ORANGUTAN
MACAQUE
LEMUR
GORILLA
NORMAN

L	G	O	E	Y	A	L	L	i	R	O	G
M	E	i	G	M	O	N	K	E	Y	R	U
A	B	M	i	Q	C	O	B	A	O	O	A	M
R	B	Q	U	U	H	R	B	Y	O	N	E
M	A	N	D	R	i	L	L	E	B	G	M
O	L	O	O	Q	M	A	C	A	Q	U	E
S	L	B	R	U	P	M	B	Y	K	T	J
E	i	B	A	R	M	O	S	E	T	A	O
T	R	i	G	O	O	O	B	A	B	N	N
M	A	G	U	N	N	O	R	M	A	N	K

GONE IN A FLASH

Now you see him...now you don't! Captain Flash has disappeared and left only shadows behind. Which one matches the real Captain Flash exactly?

PET PANDEMONIUM

Cleaning time at CitiPets has gone all wrong! How many pets in the first picture are missing from the second picture?

WISH YOU WERE HERE

Design some postcards to send home from the best trips you can imagine.

GREETINGS FROM

THE ULTIMATE DREAM DESTINATION!

SHERIFF'S SUDOKU

Help the Sheriff fill in the grid so that every row, column,
and mini-grid contains one of each symbol.

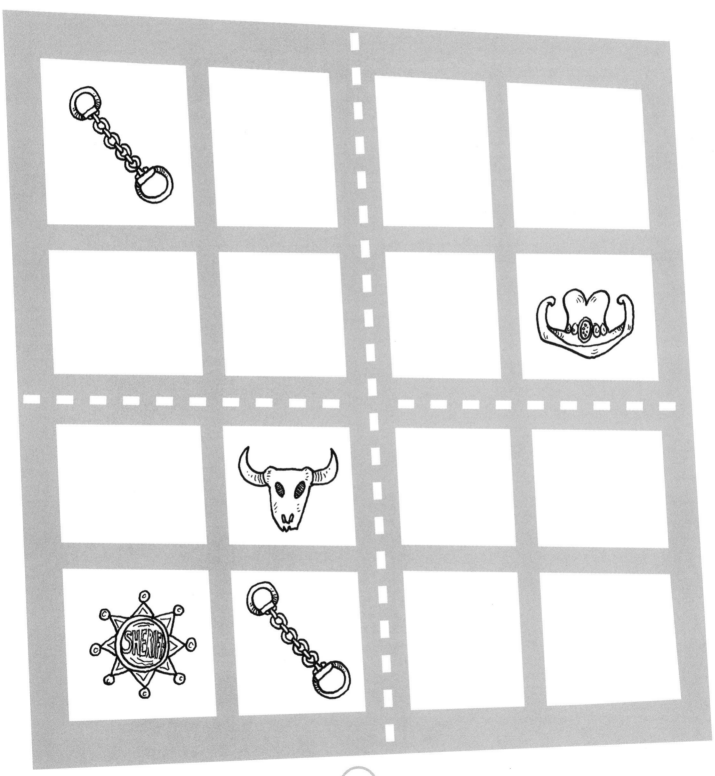

SPORTS SORT

The equipment room needs organizing, and everything must be sorted into pairs. What goes with what?

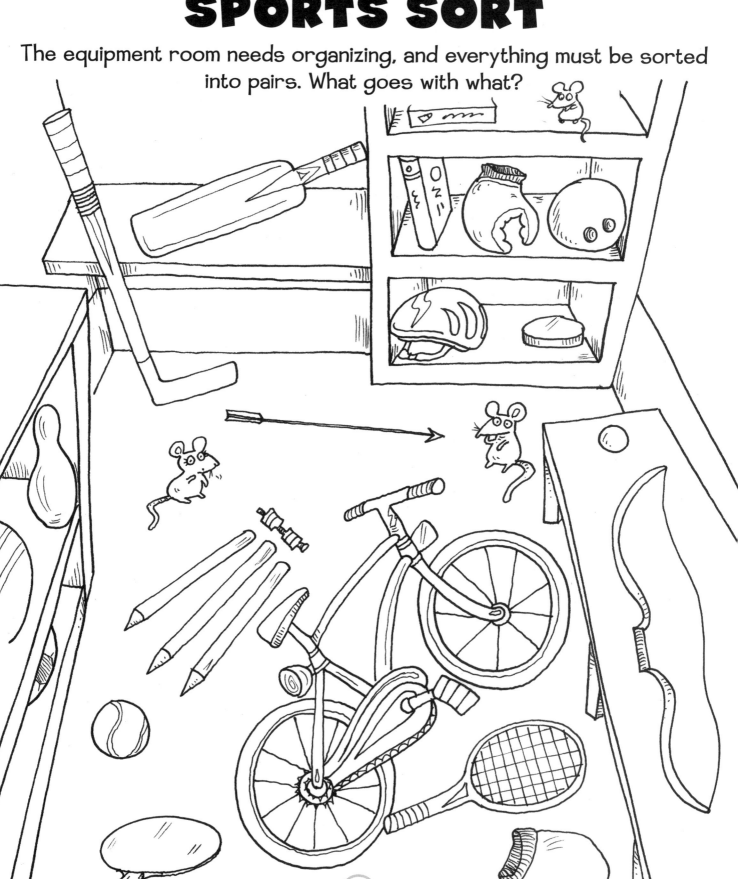

PAW PRINTS

Rearrange each set of letters to find out which
animals made these paw prints.

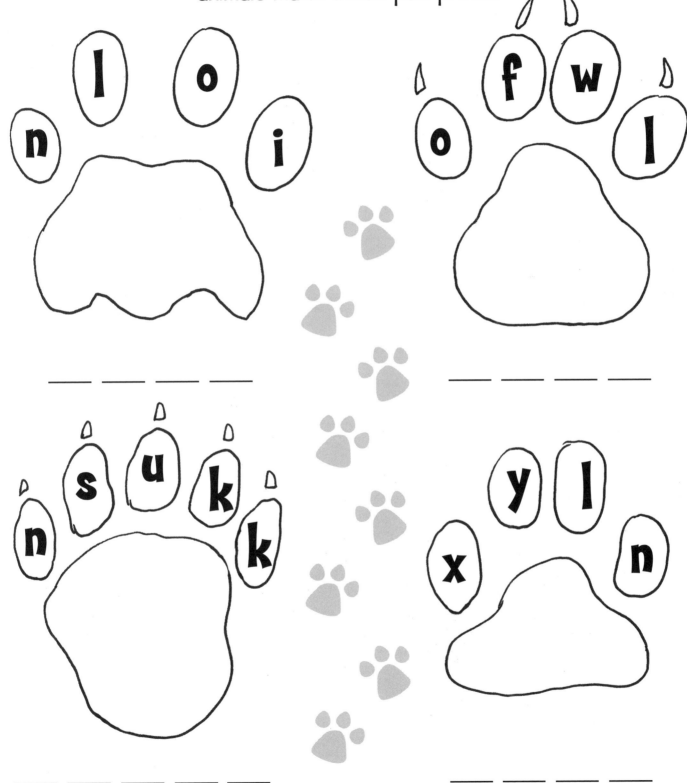

_ _ _ _

_ _ _ _

_ _ _ _ _

_ _ _ _ _

COMIC STRIP

Rearrange the pictures of Super Horace so that they tell the story in the correct order.

BRAIN TEASER

Use the clues to figure out which person owns each pet, and what those pets are named.

	Cat	Gerbil	Pony
Carl			
Susie			
Grace			

Susie doesn't own a gerbil.

Her pet isn't named Peppa.

The cat is owned by a girl.

Carl's pet is named Hector.

Grace is afraid of horses.

The largest pet is named Crystal.

Carl's pet is smaller than Grace's.

	Cat	Gerbil	Pony
Crystal			
Peppa			
Hector			

189

CHOCOHOLICS

Can you find the one chocolate that is not the same shape
as any of the others?

SPOON SEARCH

How many spoons can you count in this Wild West picture?

BACK OF THE NET!

What sport is being played on this field? Draw some players
and their equipment - either real or made up!

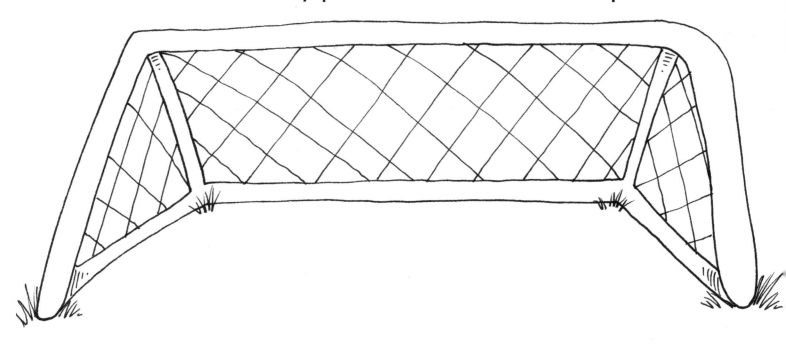

"C" CREATURES

How many living creatures can you think of that begin with the letter C? See if you can think of eight or more!

1. _____

2. _____

3. _____

4. _____

5. _____

6. _____

7. _____

8. _____

9. _____

10. _____

A COOL CLIMBER

The Great Gecko can climb walls like you wouldn't believe! Find a way up this glass building, using only numbers that are multiples of four.

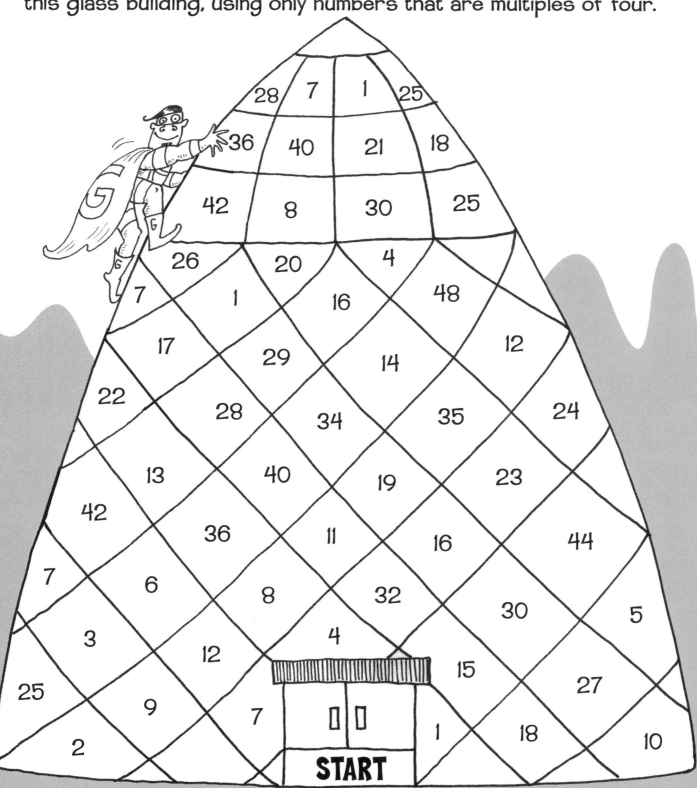

YOU CHOOSE

It's hard to choose a pet when they're all so cute! Pick the two guinea pigs that are exactly the same.

IN A STATE

Use the clue letters to fit the US states into the correct places on the grid. The circled letters will then spell out another state.

ALABAMA   **NEW YORK**

ARIZONA   **MONTANA**

FLORIDA   **WYOMING**

GEORGIA

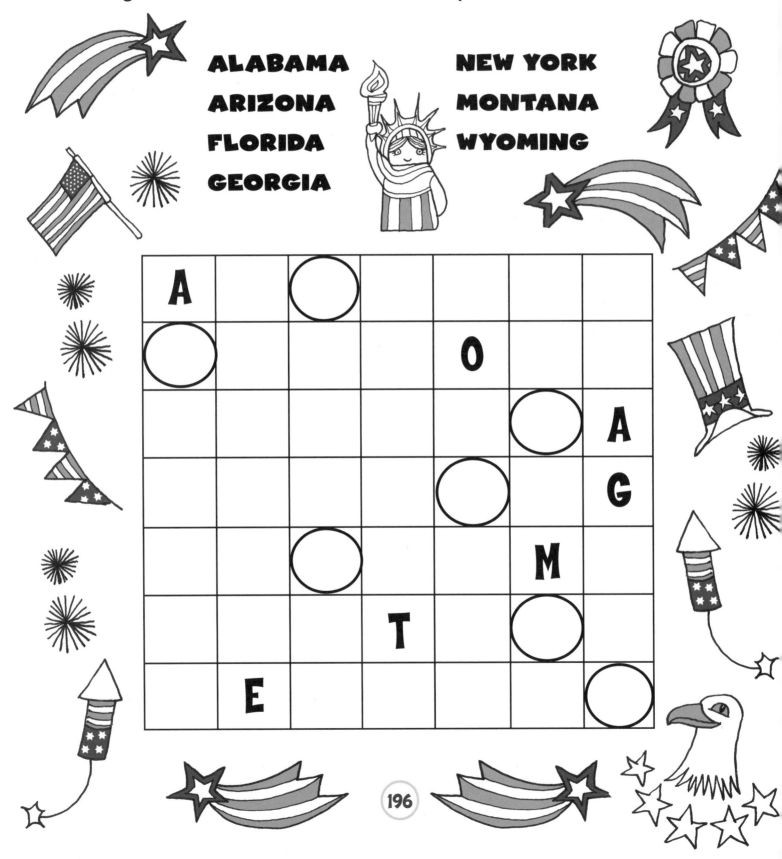

QUICK ON THE DRAW

Look carefully at the mixed-up picture. Draw each of the squares in the correct place on the grid to put the picture back together again.

CROSS OUT

Follow the instructions to find the answer to the joke.

Why did the golfer have an extra pair of socks?

in	because	sometimes	only	whenever
before	case	caddy	he	wanted
could	mostly	bad	got	lazy
a	crazy	fields	dirty	hole
in	grass	bunker	really	bird
useless	bottom	one	bat	plenty

1. Cross out words with five or more letters.
2. Get rid of any word that ends in Y.
3. Lose the words beginning with B.

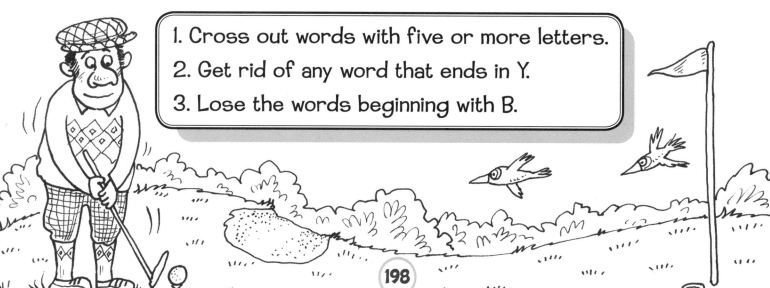

SAFARI TRAIL

Find a way along the dusty paths to the safari lodge, making sure you pass each animal only once. You aren't allowed to drive on the same path twice!

199

SUPER WHO?

Who's this flying through the skies? You decide! Give the hero a name, a costume, and his own special superpower.

A TRICKY QUESTION

It's difficult to decide what to name a pet! Look along every row to find the one letter that appears in each name. Find all eight letters to spell the name of Cassie's horse.

Asha	Harry	Micah	Hunter	___
Jessie	Severus	Pepe	Ember	___
Rex	Trojan	Bryce	Sparky	___
Scrappy	Che	Scooter	Archer	___
Furby	Cutie	Puma	Hudson	___
Macklin	Laddie	Lennox	Clover	___
Neo	Ennis	Nelson	Ike	___
Storm	Carson	Skipper	Usher	___

201

TRAIN TREK

Study the train schedule to help Richie figure out the answers to his questions.

PARIS - MILAN - ROME

Paris	departs	10:41	11:05	2:41	4:35	7:45
Milan	arrives	5:56	6:17	9:56	11:47	5:38
	departs	7:20	8:12	11:20	1:12	6:45
Rome	arrives	10:45	11:56	2:45	4:56	1:24

1. What time does the first train leave from Paris?   _____

2. How long does it take to travel from Paris to Milan on the 2:41 train?   _____

3. If Richie wants to arrive in Milan just before midnight, what time should he leave Paris?   _____

4. Which is the slowest train from Paris to Milan?   _____

5. How long will Richie have to wait in Milan if he wants to go from Paris to Rome at 11:05?   _____

202

SAY WHAT?

Use the key to figure out what on earth
this cowboy is talking about!

SADDLE   HIT   WORK   END   HORSE   ON   MY   BONE

IT'S   UP   AND   TAIL   THE   COW   TRAIL

_____   _____   _____

_____   _____   _____

EXTREME THRILLS

As the sun sets on the mountains, look carefully to see which of these snowboarder silhouettes exactly matches the main picture.

STINKY SUMS

Fill in the number pyramid on the dung beetle balls to find out how many tons of food a wild African elephant can eat every year!

To fill in the numbers, add two circles that are side by side, and write the answer in the circle above them.
One has been done to show you how: 3 + 11 = 14

ON THE MOVE

Follow the lines from Mighty Mo's hands to rearrange the letters. When they're in the right order, the letters will spell her uncanny superpower!

i E R A M i D G N D N

COLLARED

How many dog collars are scattered on this page?

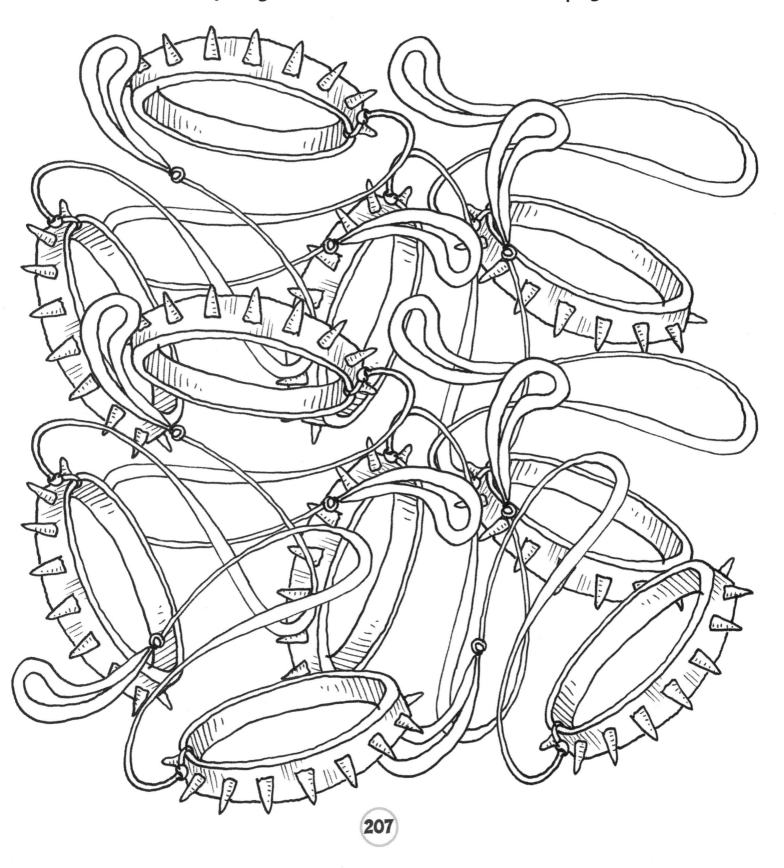

ROOM WITH A VIEW

What would you see out of your hotel window on your dream trip?

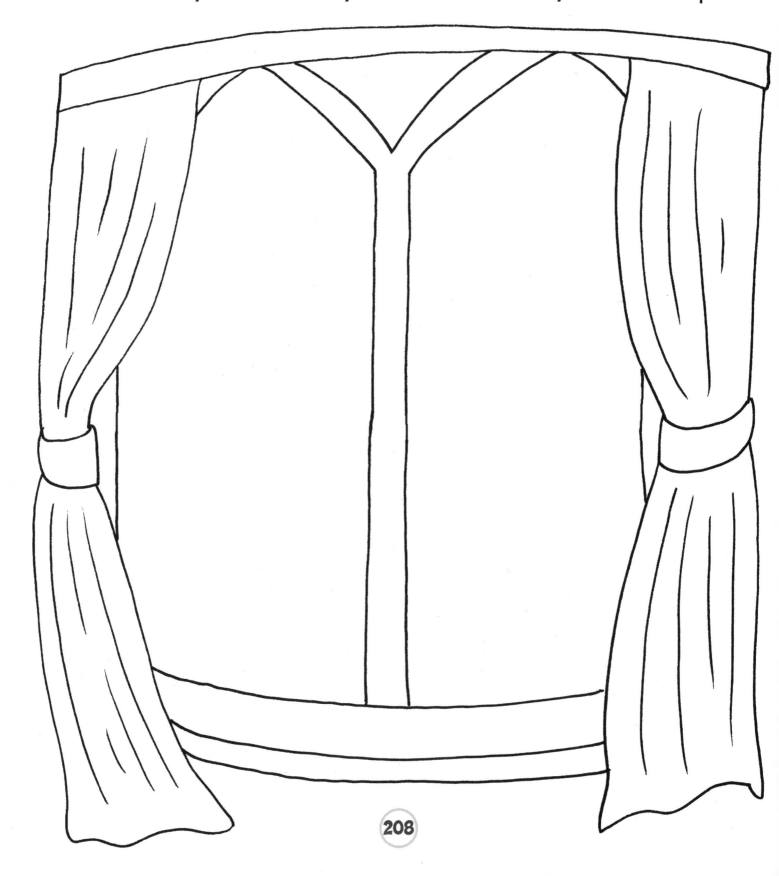

THE WILD WEST

Use the map of Bonanza City to answer the questions below.

1. In which square is the Sheriff's office?

2. What is for sale in E1?

3. If you follow the road from B3 to A4, what do you pass on your right?

4. Which square can you visit to buy a new saddle?

BOUNCE AROUND

Bounce from one ball to the next, following them in the direction of the arrows and in this order:

1. 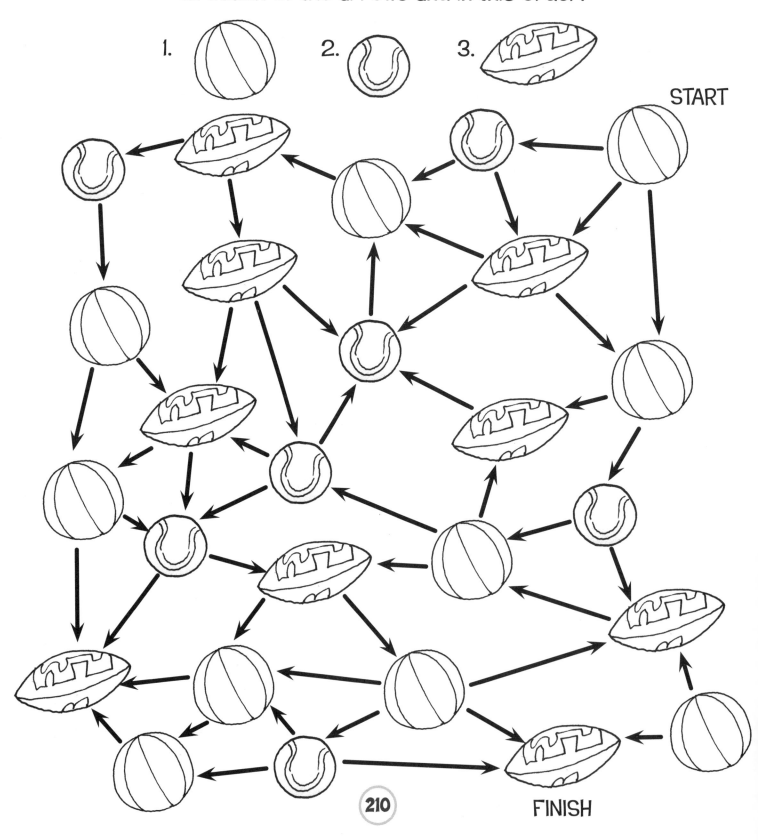 2. 3.

START

210

FINISH

CRITTER LITTERS

A set of babies born at the same time is called a litter.
Link each mother to her babies, passing through the equation whose
answer is the correct number for each litter.

53 - 46

(12x12) - 132

(9x9) - 80

45 ÷ 5

60 ÷ 12

(8x6) ÷ 24

FLYING HIGH

Rita von Clapp is trapped on the balcony of a skyscraper!
Figure out which of the smaller pictures is the view Astrogirl
has as she flies over the city to rescue her.

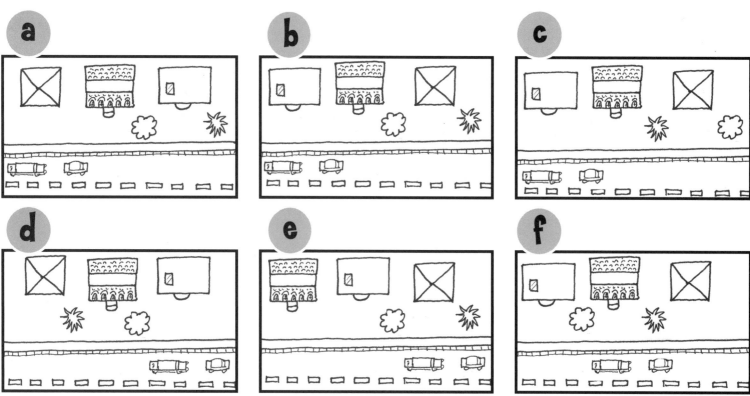

PET PUZZLER

Figure out which clue describes each pet, and write the number in the correct square. All of the rows, columns, and diagonals should add up to 15.

1. A pet with gills

2. This pet carries its own home around

3. Can be tabby or ginger

4. A master of disguise

5. A pet with no legs

6. This pet needs lots of walks

7. It might talk to you!

8. A squeaky creature

9. Has long ears and a twitchy nose

CAUGHT ON CAMERA

Look carefully at Suki's photo of the pool
to find each of the people circled below.

BEHIND BARS

Crack the number code to help Lola Starr get her true love out of jail.

1. 55 ÷ 11

2. 75 - 68

3. 3 x 3

4. 150 ÷ 50

ANYONE FOR TENNIS?

Can you find the word BALL hidden just once in the grid below?

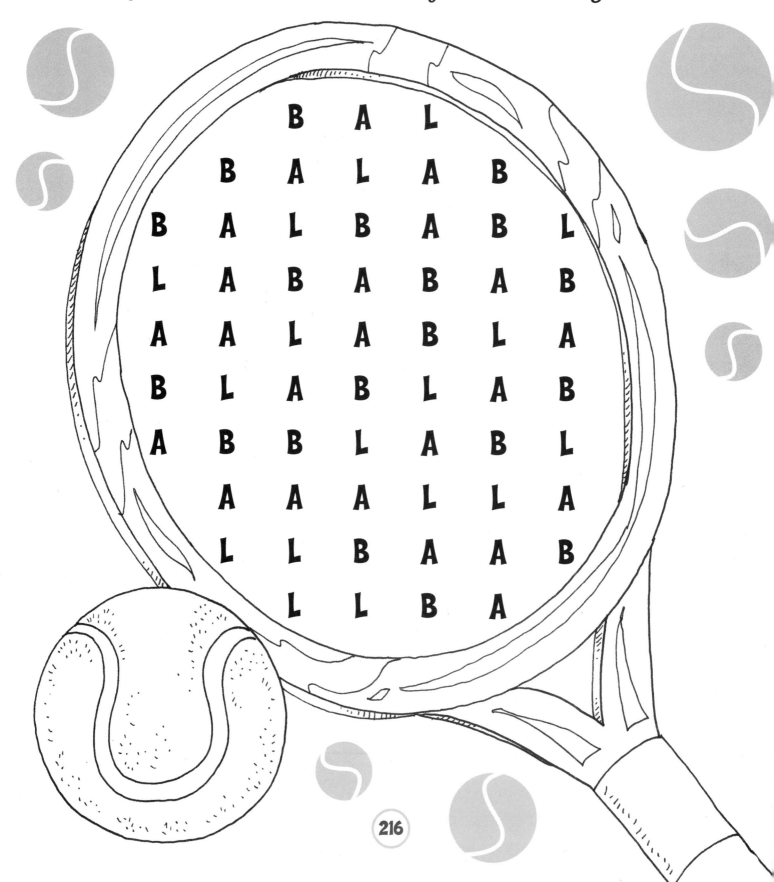

```
    B   A   L
  B   A   L   A   B
B   A   L   B   A   B   L
L   A   B   A   B   A   B
A   A   L   A   B   L   A
B   L   A   B   L   A   B
A   B   B   L   A   B   L
    A   A   A   L   L   A
    L   L   B   A   A   B
        L   L   B   A
```

TRAIL FINDER

Draw who - or what - you think has made these footprints.

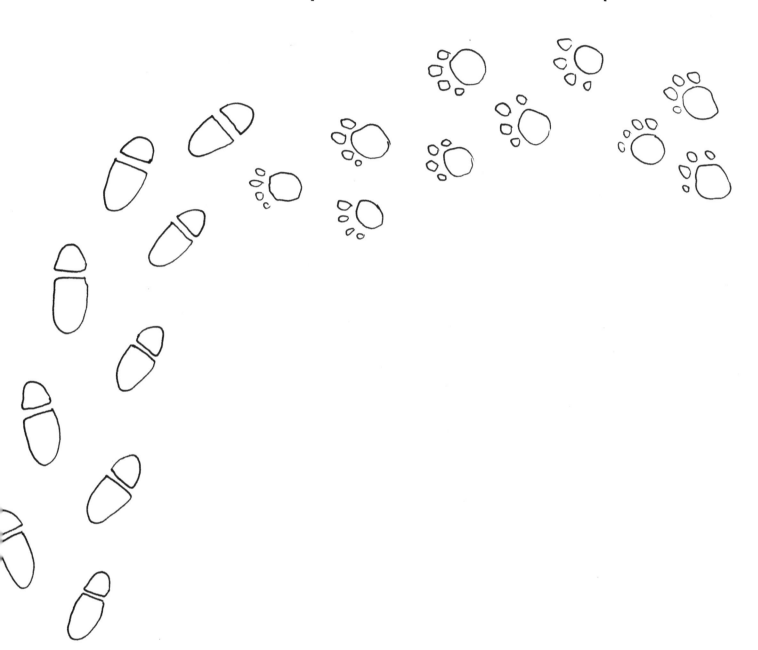

SUPER TROOPER

Use the grid references to write down the correct letters.
They will spell out Trooper X's superpower!

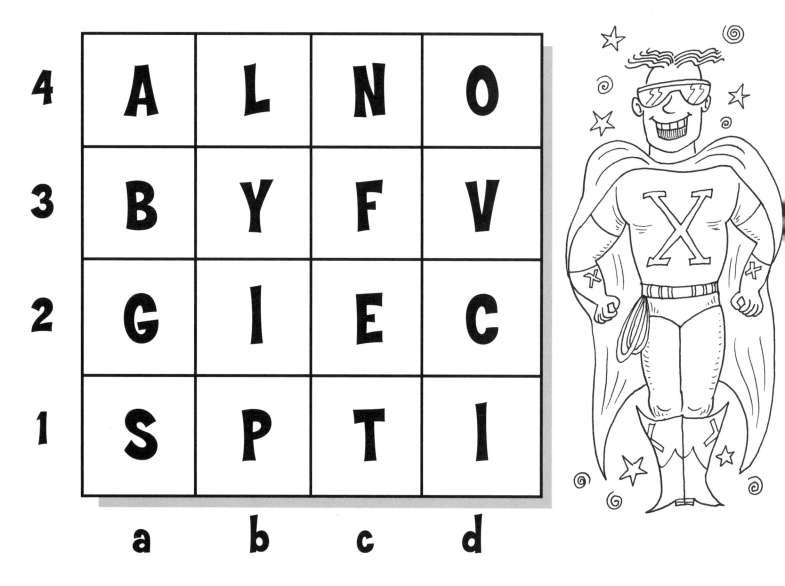

	a	b	c	d
4	A	L	N	O
3	B	Y	F	V
2	G	I	E	C
1	S	P	T	I

b2 c4 d3 b2 a1 d1 a3 b2 b4 d1 c1 b3

_ _ _ _ _ _ _ _ _ _ _ _

FLY AWAY HOME

Follow each bird to find out who they belong to.

LOST LUGGAGE

Help the baggage handlers at Totally Brilliant airport find the correct suitcase for Mrs. Rumpleton.

a  SMT

b  LTC

h  BLR

c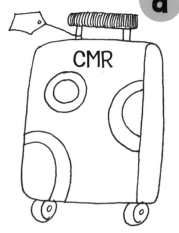

1. Her case has wheels.

2. It has a label tied to the handle.

3. Her initials are on the case.

4. The handle is dark.

d  CMR

g

f

e

WAGON WHEELS

Use the letters on each wheel to spell six Wild West words.

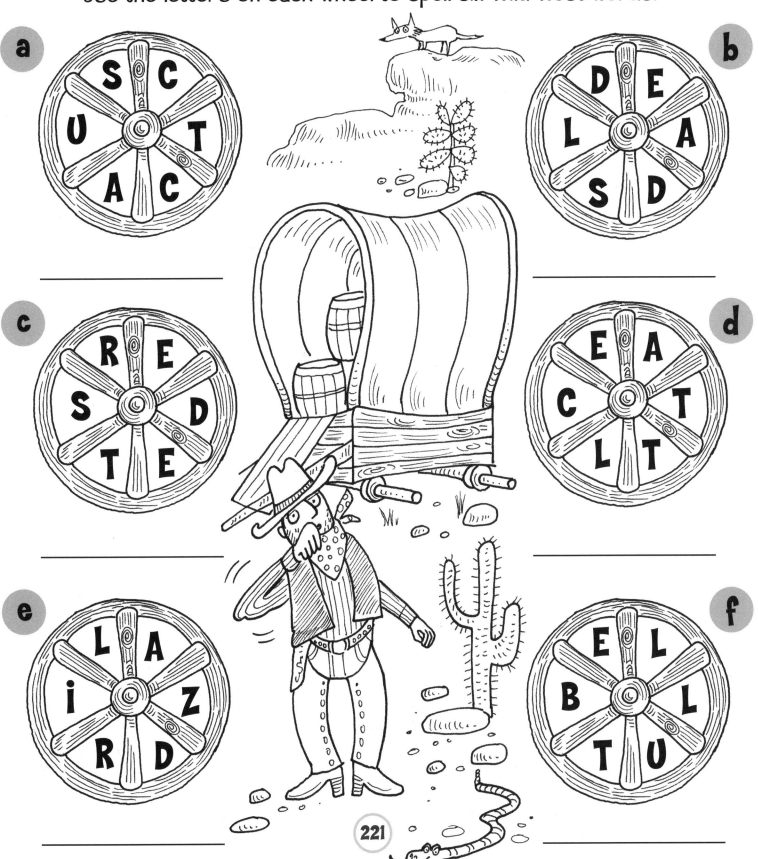

a

b

c

d

e

f

SLAM DUNK

Alley-oop like a pro and guide the ball through the net maze!

LEAPING LEMURS!

Four of these lemurs are exactly the same. Can you find them?

SUPER SPELLINGS

How many words can you create from the letters below?
One has been done to help you get started.

SILVER SORCERESS

1. _river_
2. _____
3. _____
4. _____
5. _____
6. _____
7. _____
8. _____
9. _____
10. _____
11. _____
12. _____
13. _____
14. _____
15. _____
16. _____

224

TROPICAL TANK

This fish tank is too empty. Can you draw some fabulous fish
and add some furniture for them to swim around?

CYPRUS SUDOKU

Fill in the blanks using the letters CYPRUS, in any order, so that every row, column, and mini-grid contains each letter only once.

P	Y	C			
U	R	S		P	
S	C	Y			
			C	Y	S
	S		P	C	
			U		Y

AMBUSHED!

Big "Tone" Telford has been caught in the mountain pass by Wild Mikey Armitage and his gang. Can you find ten coins hidden in the scene?

PARK LIFE

Read the map and use the grid references to help you
answer the questions about the sports park.

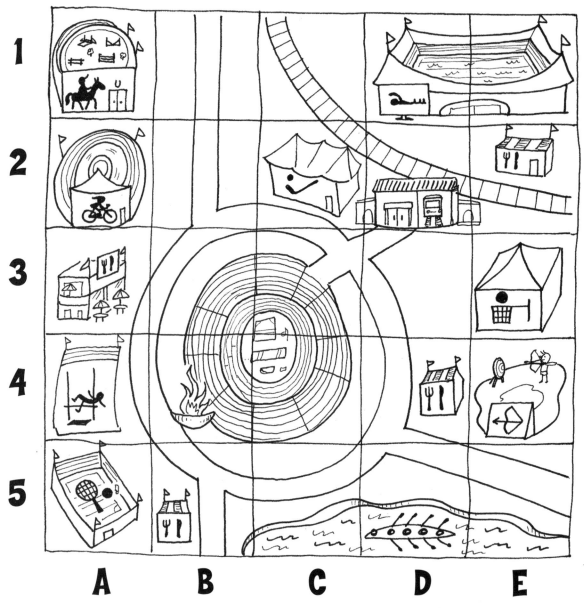

1. In which square is the train station?

2. What sport can you see in E4?

3. Where is the closest place to eat if you have watched cycling?

4. Which of these does not have an entrance to the main stadium: C3, B5, C2, or B2?

5. What event is taking place in A5?

6. If you want to watch rowing, should you head to D1 or D5?

CUTE CUBS

Which of these cheeky cheetahs is different from the rest?

ON THE RUN

Start at the bomb and follow the letters to find six things a superhero wears. The leftover letters will spell the runaway villain's name.

PCAPEAGLOVESRBOO
SAMDTIUSAST
SKOBELTX

NETTED

Study the two pictures to see which three fish from the top picture have been caught and taken to a new home.

RIDING HIGH

How many times can you find the word ALPS hidden in the grid?

```
    L  A  P  S
 A  L  P  A  P
 P  P  S  L  A  A
A  L  P  S  P  A  L
L  P  A  L  S  S  P
P  L  A  A  L  L  S
 S  L  A  L  A  P
 A  P  P  S  P  S
 L  S  A  L  P  S
 S  L  A  P  S  A
```

DRESS TO IMPRESS

Decorate this Native American headdress so it's fit for a chief.

233

STICK WITH IT

How many hockey sticks are jumbled in this picture?

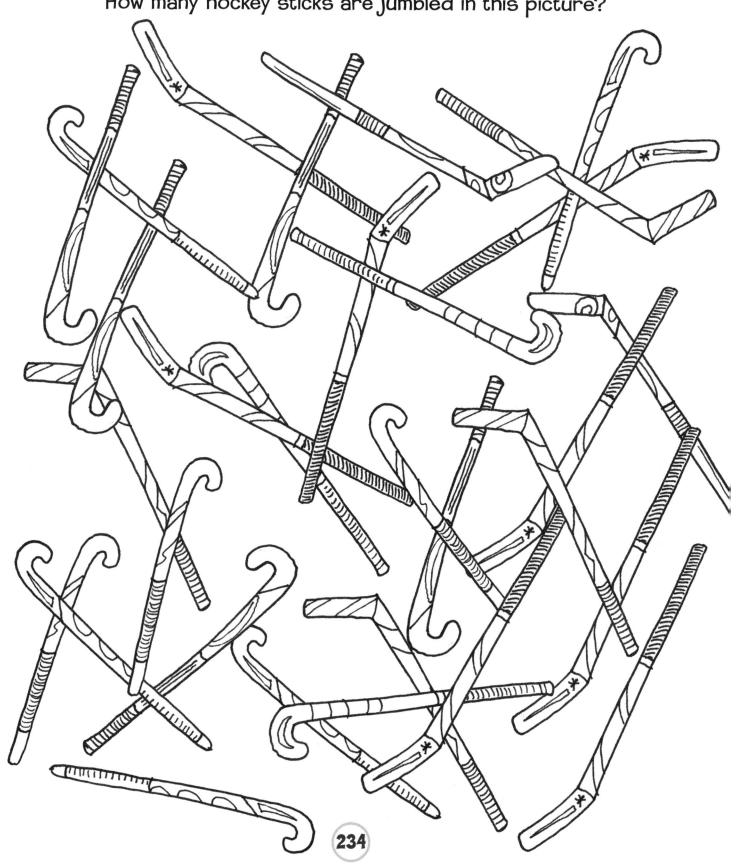

SSSSSSILLY SSSSSSTUFF

Shade in all the squares containing S, E, and D.
The remaining letters will spell the answer to the joke.

What happened to the snake that swallowed a set of keys?

S	E	E	D	S	D	E	S	S	E
D	S	i	D	E	S	E	E	D	S
E	E	D	E	S	S	T	D	E	S
S	E	D	S	E	D	D	E	E	S
D	G	E	E	O	S	E	D	E	D
E	D	S	E	D	S	E	E	T	S
S	E	D	D	E	S	D	S	D	E
L	E	D	O	C	E	E	K	E	D
S	S	J	D	D	E	A	E	S	W
D	E	S	D	S	D	E	S	S	D	E	S

_____

235

SUPER SHOOTERS

Use only the letters from the guns shooting to the left to find out what Krall the Conqueror's superpower is.

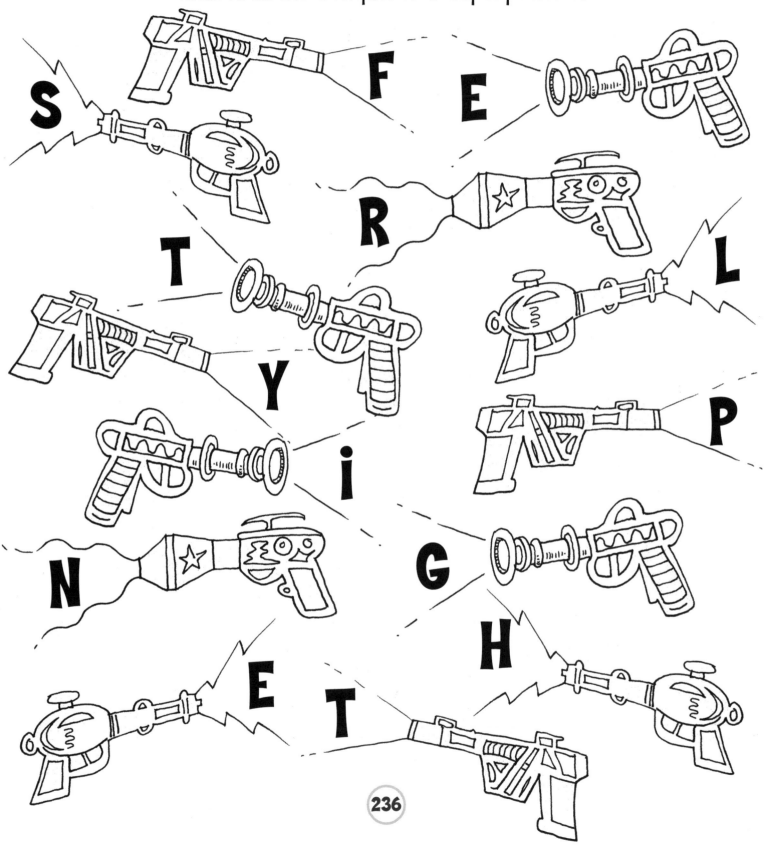

JUST JOKING

Follow the instructions to find the answer to the joke.

Why are cats good at video games?

so	when	because	they
kick	squeak	should	always
save	have	with	back
twenty	stick	nine	lick
clock	lives	paws	whiskers

1. Get rid of words that begin with S.
2. Cross out any word with W in it.
3. Don't use words ending in K.

CIAO ITALIA!

Julia is visiting Italy to see the famous sights.
The letters missing from the alphabet at each landmark
spell out which cities she goes to.

BCDEFGHJKLMN
OQRTUVWXYZ

ABCDFGHIJKLNP
QSTUVWXYZ

BCDEFGHJKOPQ
RSTUVWXYZ

BCDFGHIJKMOQ
RTUVWXYZ

POWWOW, NOW!

A powwow gives Native Americans the chance to dance and celebrate in a traditional way. As night begins to fall, find the shadow that matches the main picture.

DREAM TEAM

Design a uniform for the sports team you support.
Base it on their real one, or make up your own.

EAGLE EYES

See if you can find the smaller squares somewhere in the main picture.
Write the grid reference for each one.

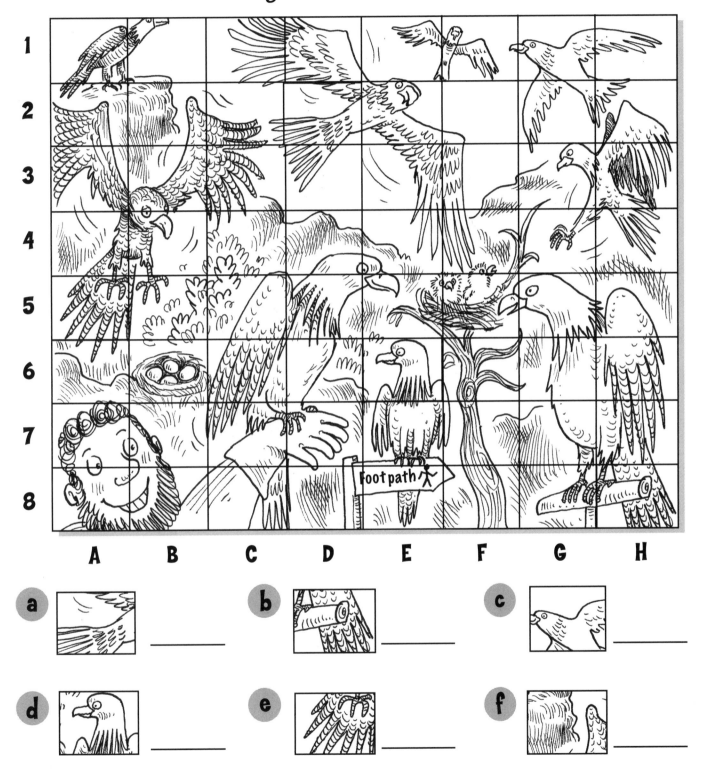

BETTER, FASTER, HIGHER

Which of these superheroes can fly the highest? Add up the numbers below each one to find out. The biggest total wins!

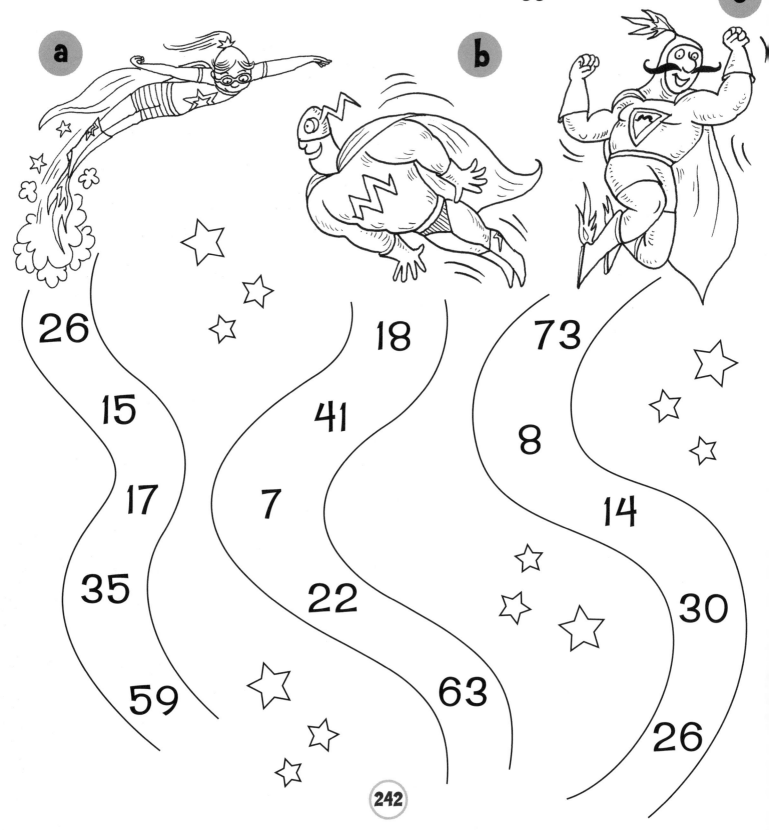

a

26
15
17
35
59

b

18
41
7
22
63

c

73
8
14
30
26

IT'S A MYSTERY

There are 20 pets hidden in this wordsearch grid, but no clues to help you find them! Look for them up, down, across, and diagonally.

F	T	i	B	B	A	R	R	A	T	F	S
G	O	L	D	F	i	S	H	S	P	D	N
U	E	H	R	T	T	G	L	N	R	T	A
i	D	R	A	P	O	E	i	A	C	E	i
N	U	C	B	M	R	R	Z	K	H	R	L
E	K	H	B	i	S	i	A	E	i	R	O
A	C	i	G	C	L	T	L	i	Z	A	F
P	N	M	Z	A	G	F	E	R	R	P	E
i	E	O	i	O	L	Y	M	R	Y	i	R
G	K	U	D	i	R	J	i	N	A	N	R
P	C	S	E	A	O	U	O	H	D	F	E
A	i	E	N	D	G	P	A	R	R	O	T
R	H	A	S	T	O	R	T	O	i	S	E
R	C	H	i	N	C	H	i	L	L	A	D

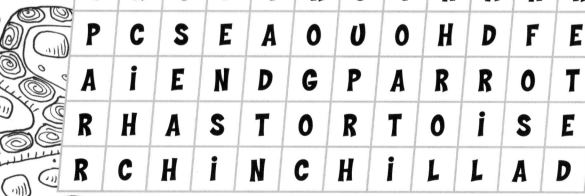

243

FUN IN THE SUN

Figure out which clue describes each item, and write the number in the correct square. All of the rows, columns, and diagonals should add up to 15.

1. Fashion for your face

2. Flying high

3. A juicy treat

4. Digging it!

5. Pretty but fragile

6. Yum in the sun!

7. Goes with 4

8. Speedy swimmers

9. A little pincher

PICK A POLE

Which of these totem poles is the odd one out?

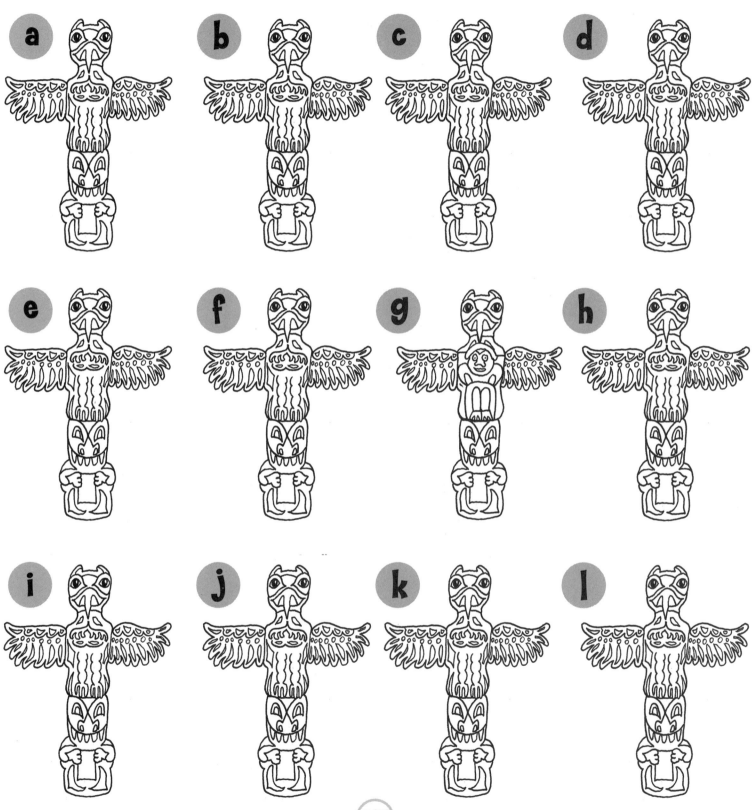

BOWLED OVER

Add up the numbers on the pins to find out the total score.

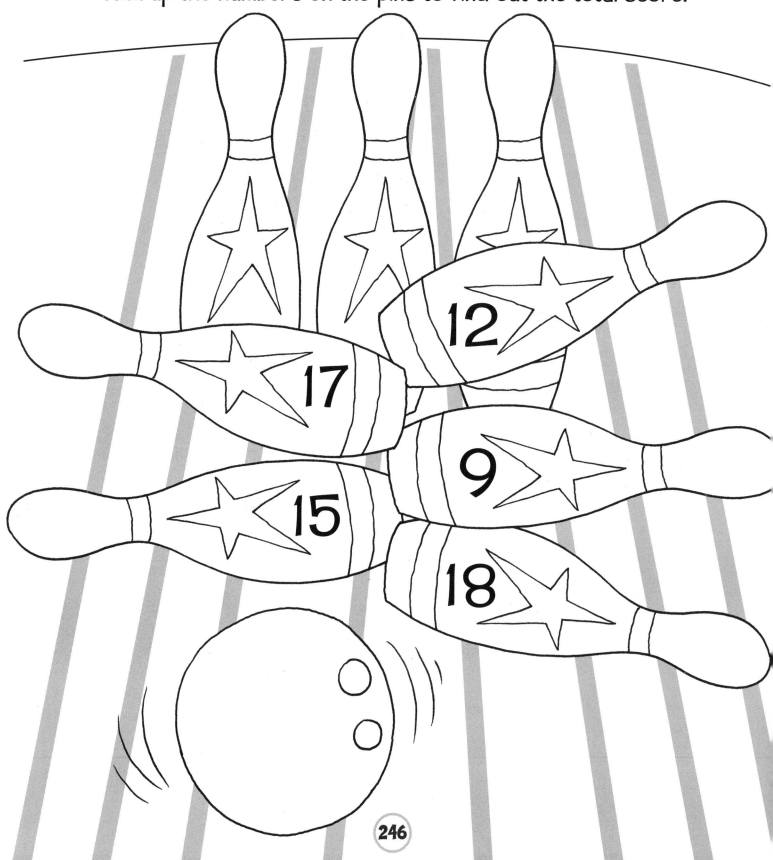

TIME TO EAT!

Use the letters on the clock to figure out which zoo animals are expecting their food at the times shown. Follow the instructions in the box.

> Write down the letters shown by the minute hand, then by the hour hand, for each time listed below. The letters will spell an animal's name. For example, quarter to five = LION.

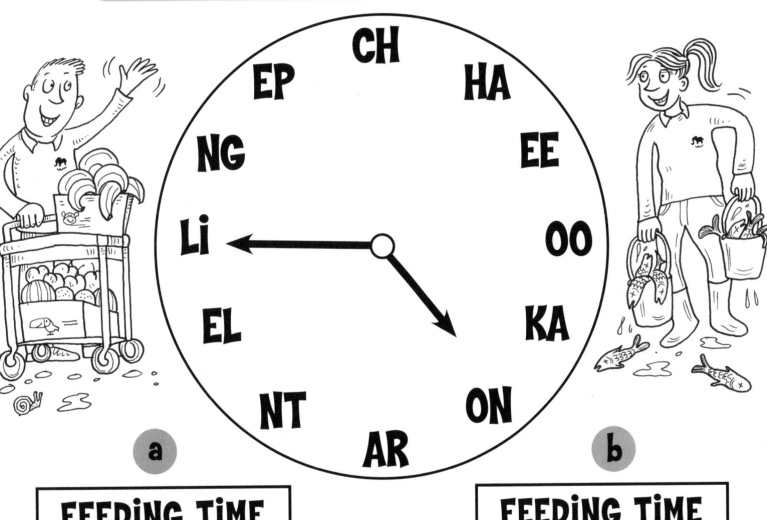

a

FEEDING TIME

_____

fed at twenty to eleven
and
five past seven

b

FEEDING TIME

_____

fed at twenty past ten
and
half past three

X-RAY VISION

Imagine you are a superhero with X-ray eyes. That's right, you can see right through things! What is this bad guy carrying in his bag?

MUCKING OUT

Ferdy loves her pony so much, she doesn't even mind mucking out the stable! Can you find 10 carrots hidden in this picture?

ON THE CASE

Helen has forgotten the code to open her suitcase. Can you help her to figure it out?

1. Days in May minus days in June
2. Legs on a flamingo times the number of blind mice
3. Hours in a day divided by half a dozen
4. Legs on a spider minus Goldilocks' bears

THE OLD WEST

Cross out any letter that appears more than once. The remaining letters
will spell the name of a true cowboy state in the USA.

ON YOUR BIKE

Circle every third letter on the mountain bike track to discover
a type of cycling, sometimes known as XC.

BIRD BRAINS

Find all 25 feathered friends in this giant word search puzzle.

E	A	L	B	A	T	R	O	S	S	E	P	C	P
H	M	W	O	O	D	W	T	O	U	C	H	T	I
W	E	U	C	U	L	C	K	O	O	A	E	H	G
E	R	R	H	O	R	N	B	I	L	L	A	R	E
A	P	E	N	G	U	I	N	P	W	B	S	U	O
G	E	N	N	G	R	E	B	E	E	I	A	S	N
L	K	I	O	B	P	E	L	I	C	A	N	H	I
E	O	S	T	R	I	C	H	P	E	D	T	T	B
W	O	O	D	P	E	C	K	E	R	H	O	U	O
O	K	R	O	B	D	H	R	T	S	O	U	V	R
R	C	D	T	U	R	K	E	Y	B	R	C	W	E
C	U	U	C	P	A	R	R	O	T	N	A	R	E
A	C	K	A	L	B	F	L	A	M	I	N	G	O

TOUCAN
HORNBILL
OSTRICH
KIWI
WOODPECKER
HERON
OWL

EAGLE
EMU
DUCK
PHEASANT
ALBATROSS
GREBE

PENGUIN
FLAMINGO
PELICAN
PIGEON
DOVE
PARROT

CUCKOO
WREN
ROBIN
CROW
THRUSH
TURKEY

JEWEL THIEF

Which adversary does the Blue Comet find himself up against this time? Use the key to find out.

A B D E H i J L N O R S T U X Y

254

DOG TIRED

This pet pup has worn itself out! Look carefully on its bed to find one shape that is different from the rest.

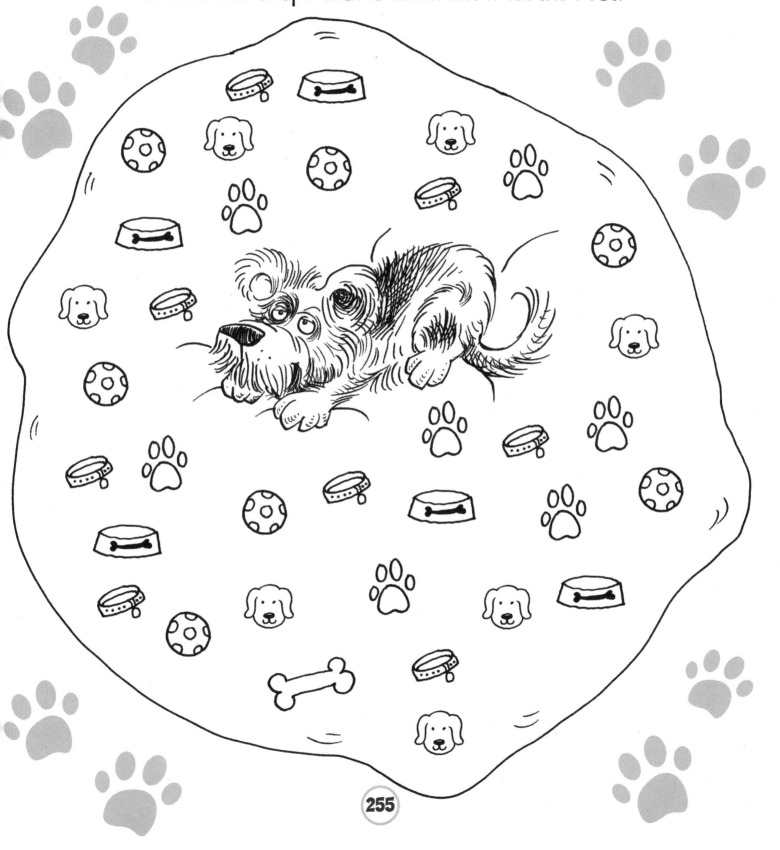

YOU'RE IN CHARGE

Imagine you're the ruler of your own country. What would your flag, money, and stamps look like?

HOME SWEET HOME

Find the smaller squares somewhere in the main picture,
and write down the grid reference for each one.

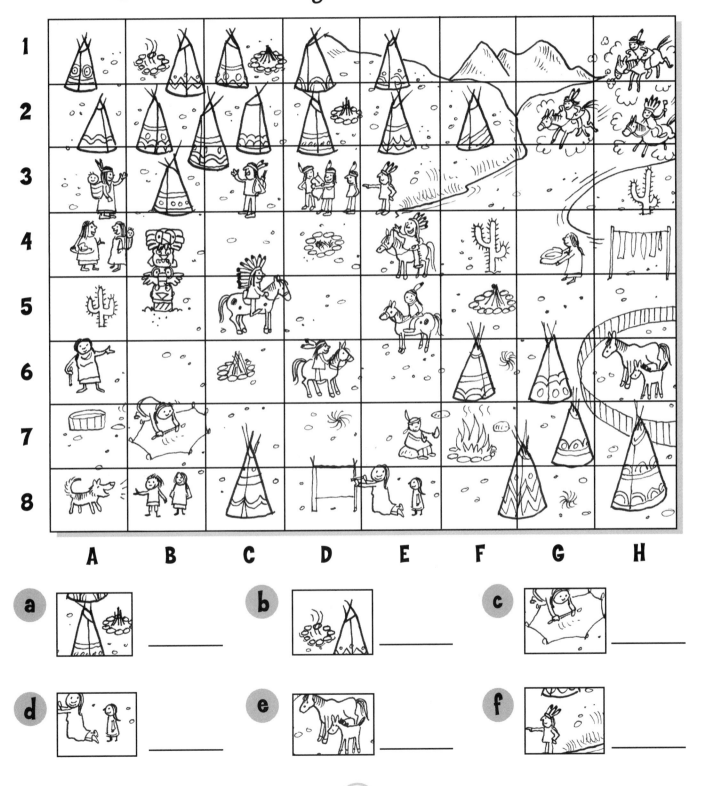

ALL THE BALLS

The mini-grid only appears once in the larger grid below. Can you find it?

ROLL UP, ROLL UP!

How many armadillos are on this page? Some of them have rolled up into a ball to hide, but you should still count them!

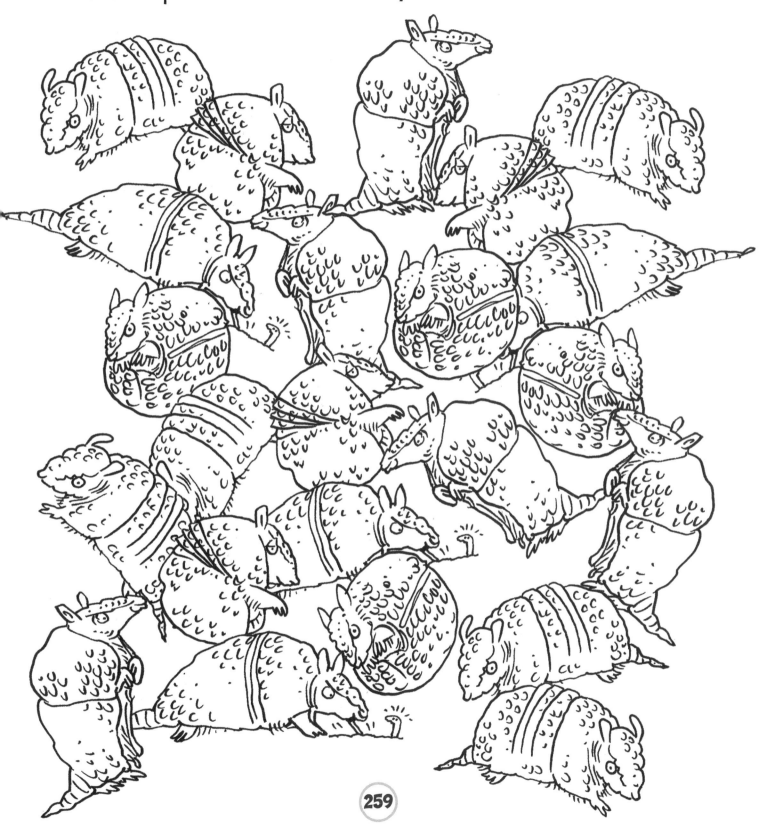

UNDERWATER RESCUE

When things go wrong in the water, you need Aquatar!
Which two superhero pictures are the same?

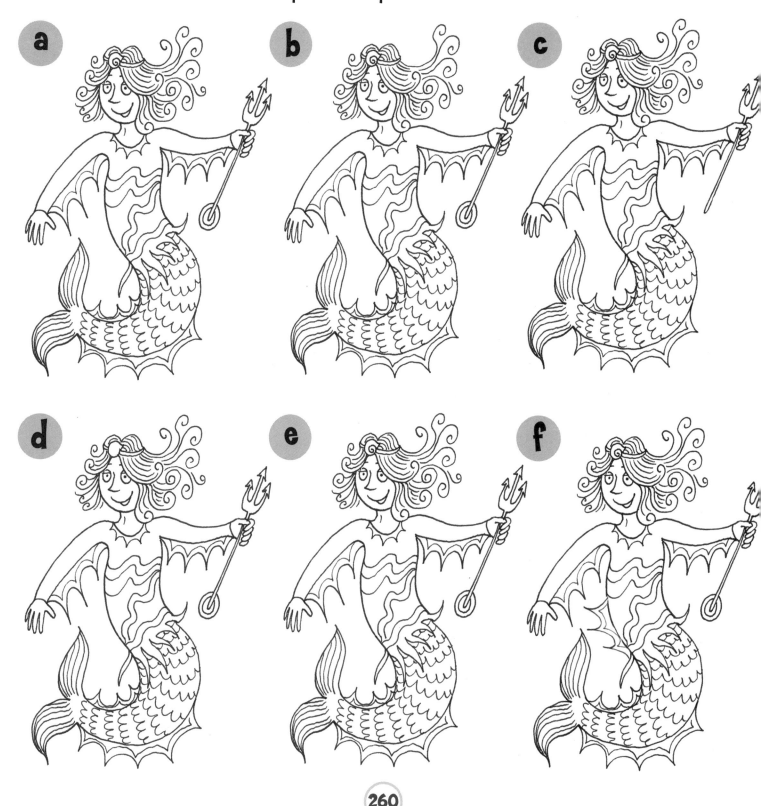

FUNNY BUNNIES

Which of the jigsaw pieces finishes the picture of the cutest bunnies you have ever seen?

DREAM TICKET

Use the grid references to write down the corresponding letters. They will spell out the place where the Martinez family is going this summer.

	a	b	c	d
4	R	S	i	E
3	K	F	N	L
2	O	W	Y	U
1	A	G	D	M

b3 d3 a2 a4 c4 c1 a1   a3 d4 c2 b4

___ ___ ___ ___ ___ ___ ___   ___ ___ ___ ___

SADDLE UP

Help the cowgirl find her way
through the desert and into
town for the rodeo.

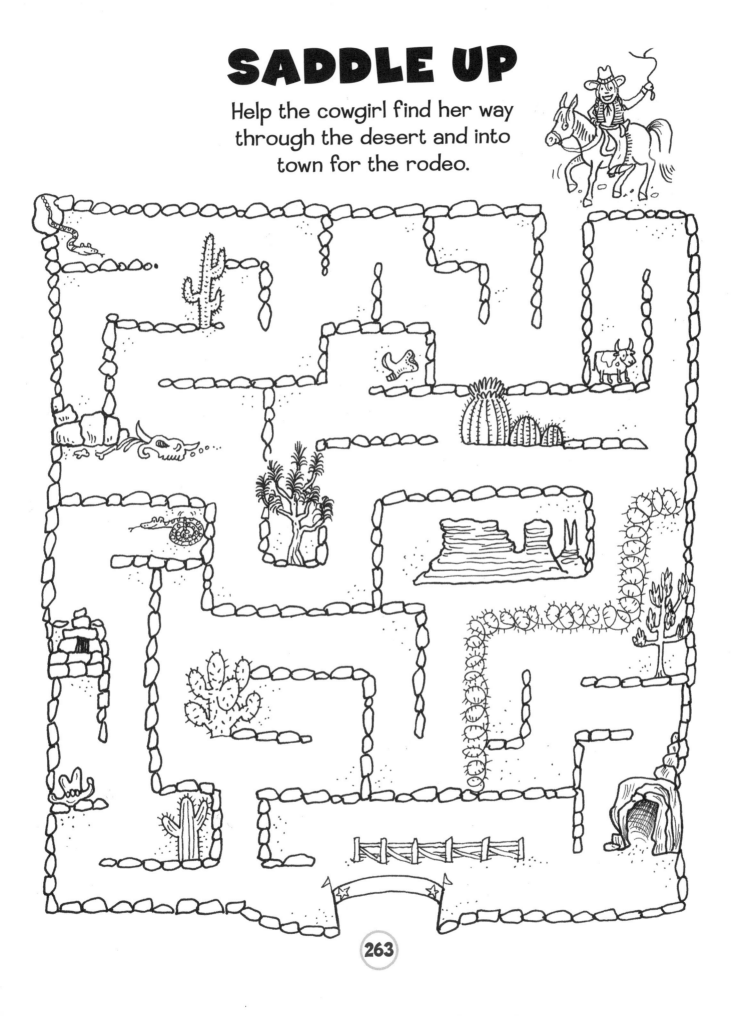

GOING FOR GOLD

Cross out all of the letters that appear twice. The remaining letters will spell a sporting superstar!

J U E S
C A I N E
R
D R T L
K
O C K
J B D

‾ ‾ ‾ ‾ ‾   ‾ ‾ ‾ ‾

HILARIOUS HYBRID

What do you think it would look like if you crossed a lion with a rhino? Or an ostrich with a penguin? Draw your silliest idea here and give it a name.

STEP ON UP!
COME AND SEE THE
INCREDIBLE _____ !

BOO! HISS!

The evil Doc Paradox has cloned himself, but one of the clones has gone slightly wrong. Which one is different from all the rest?

CUDDLY CREATURES

Study the map of the urban zoo and use it to answer the questions.

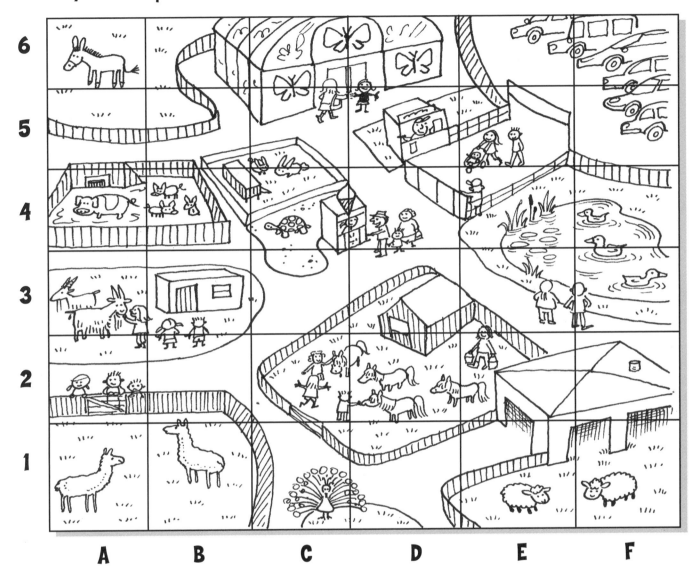

1. Which bird is roaming free in C1?

_____

2. In which square can you pet the goats?

_____

3. Where should you go to see the tortoise?

_____

4. Where is the entrance gate?

_____

5. What are the babies called in B4?

_____

6. What animal can you feed from the gate in A2?

_____

GET PACKING

Help Louisa find 10 items that go together to make 5 pairs. The other things are staying behind!

THE LONE RANGER

Can you find the word RANGER hidden just once in this grid?
Look across, up, down, and diagonally.

```
R A N G G E R E E G
A R E G A N A N R A
N A N G R A N A A G
E N A E N E N G N R
R A R R G A E A R E
A A E A E G R A N G
R E G A N G R A N R
E G N E E G A E G E
R A G E R N E N E E
G R E G A N A R G N
```

SPORTS SQUARE

Figure out which clue describes each item, and write the number in the correct square. All of the rows, columns, and diagonals should add up to 15.

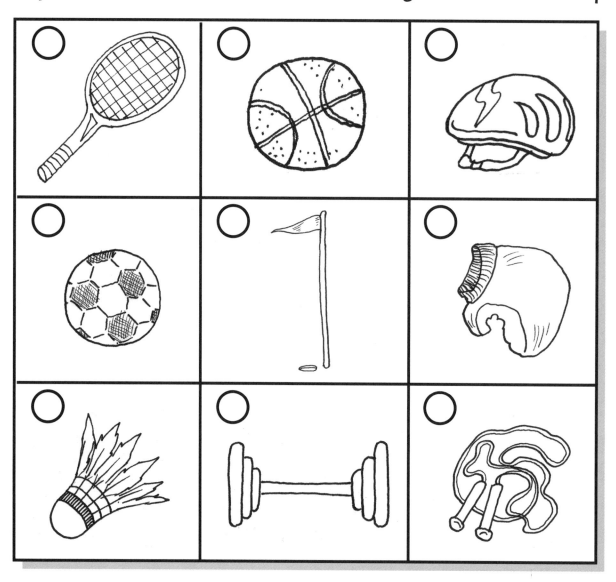

1. You wanna fight?

2. A sport with aces

3. Heavy, man!

4. Light as a feather

5. A hole in one?

6. Head case!

7. Slam dunk

8. Give it a twirl

9. Back of the net!

LION LAUGHS

Follow the instructions to find the answer to the joke.

What did the lion say when it ate the clown?

because	growl	but	huge
his	brought	did	long
not	he	she	was
back	great	tasted	breath
funny	wrong	strange	again

1. Get rid of words with three letters.
2. Cross out words containing G.
3. Lose any words that start with B.

271

TO THE RESCUE!

Omega Man and his sidekick Delta have swung into this party to save the day! How many hidden party horns can you find?

PERFECT PET

If you were allowed to have any pet in the world, what would you choose?

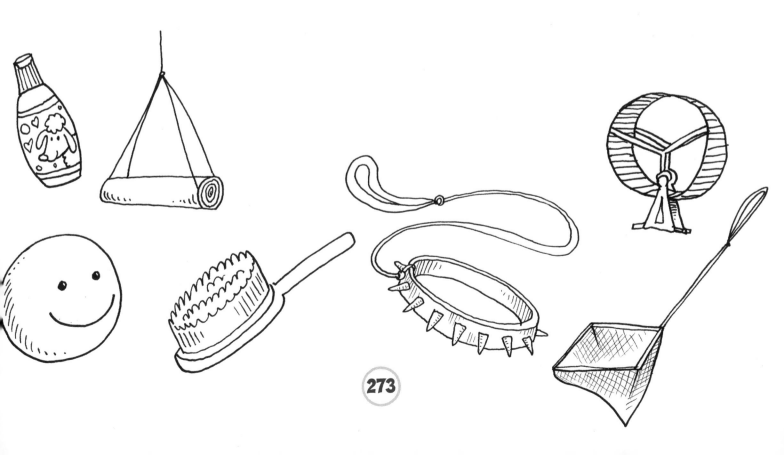

LADY LIBERTY

Welcome to the USA! Study the famous Statue of Liberty and then find which of the silhouettes is an exact match.

a

b

c

d

e

f

THE SILVER SADDLE

Welcome to the Silver Saddle Saloon! See if you can find the smaller squares somewhere in the main picture. Write the grid reference for each one.

COACH GOODWAY

What sport does Coach Goodway teach?
Use the clues to figure it out.

a

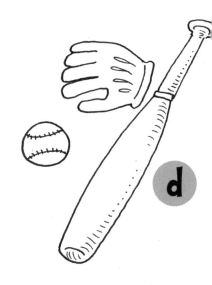

b

c

d

1. His trainees don't hit a ball.

2. The sport can be played on your own.

3. He doesn't teach you how to throw.

4. The Coach's students don't get wet!

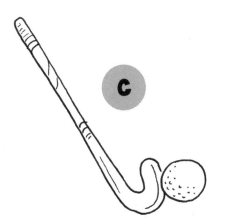

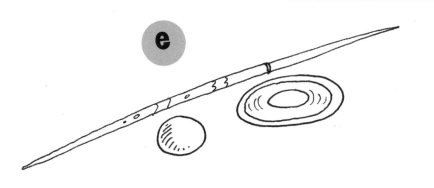

e

f

TALL AND SMALL

Look carefully at the mixed-up picture. Draw each of the squares in the correct place on the grid to put the picture back together again.

HELP ME!

Captain Schnurrbart to the rescue!
Look carefully to find six differences
between these two scenes.

278

BIRD TALK

Cross out every other letter, starting with T and moving clockwise,
to find out where this chatty pet would live in the wild.

SNORKEL SCARE

Rearrange the six pictures so that they tell the story in the correct order.

ON THE LOOKOUT

There's a new bad guy in town! Finish this Wild West wanted poster with your own cowboy criminal.

WANTED
Dead or Alive

REWARD OF
$250,000

WIN OR LOSE?

Shade in all the squares containing F, L, and O. The remaining letters will spell the answer to the joke.

Why didn't the artist ever win at sports?

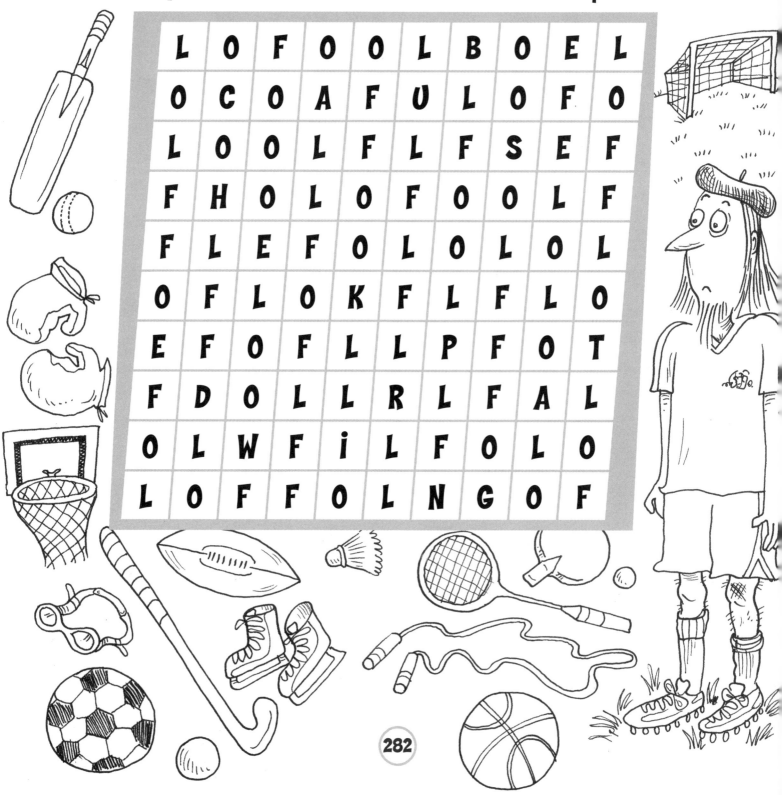

L	O	F	O	O	L	B	O	E	L
O	C	O	A	F	U	L	O	F	O
L	O	O	L	F	L	F	S	E	F
F	H	O	L	O	F	O	O	L	F
F	L	E	F	O	L	O	L	O	L
O	F	L	O	K	F	L	F	L	O
E	F	O	F	L	L	P	F	O	T
F	D	O	L	L	R	L	F	A	L
O	L	W	I	L	F	O	L	O	
L	O	F	F	O	L	N	G	O	F

282

ICE, ICE BABY

Solve the equations and find a path across the ice,
stepping only on answers that are odd numbers.

6 x 8

53 - 21

45 ÷ 5

7 x 3

24 + 54

66 - 34

16 + 19

56 ÷ 8

38 + 38

64 ÷ 8

96 - 27

7 x 6

4 x 12

11 x 3

283

SUPERFOODS

Use the grid references to write down the corresponding letters.
They will spell out Captain Cobalt's top choice on a menu.

	a	b	c	d
4	A	P	E	H
3	U	N	Y	F
2	R	E	S	B
1	M	L	C	i

d2 b1 a3 b2 d2 c4 a2 a2 c3   b4 d1 c4

_ _ _ _ _ _ _ _ _   _ _ _

IT'S A STICK UP

How many stick insects are hiding here?

BIG ADVENTURE

Use the clues to figure out what each of the girls is camping in, and where they are going.

	Tent	Camper van	Teepee
Amy			
Leigh			
Millie			

Amy isn't going to Italy.

Millie's home has wheels.

The girl in the tent is going to Spain.

Leigh and Millie aren't going to France.

	France	Italy	Spain
Amy			
Leigh			
Millie			

OUTLAWED

Billy the Kid has escaped from jail! Follow the directions to find out where he's hiding.

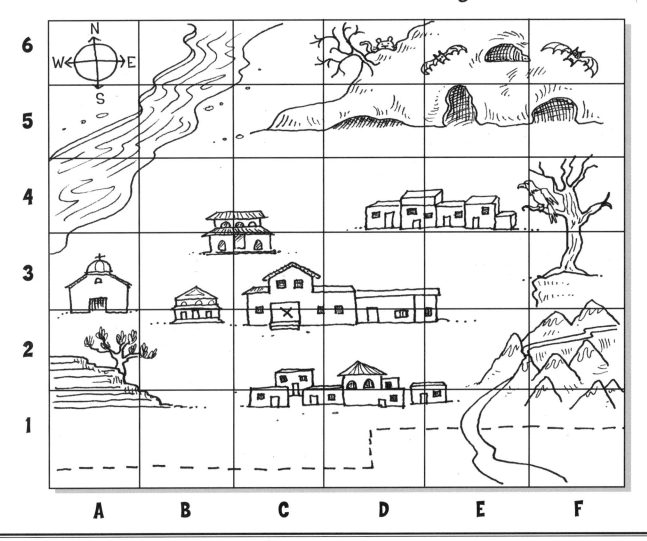

1. After leaving jail in C3, he headed 1 square south for the border, but went 2 squares east to avoid the huts.

2. At the mountains he went south again for 1 square, crossed the border, and ran 3 squares west.

3. He snuck 4 squares north, past Lone Pine Ridge and the church.

4. At the Rio Grande river he headed east 1 square, then north 1 square, then east 1 square again. Where should the sheriff look for him?

THE WINNER IS...

You decide! Draw the race winners on the podium.
They can be competitors in any sport you like.

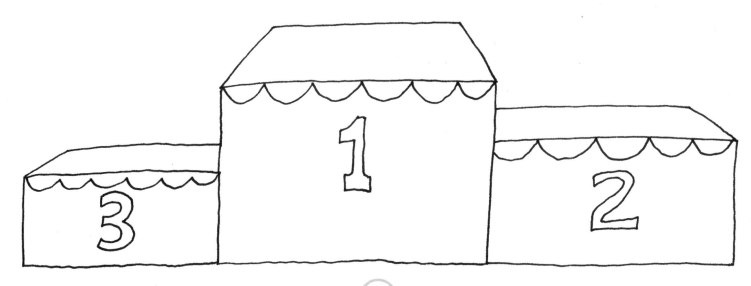

ANIMAL MIX-UP!

What on earth is a ferkey? Or a waltle? Hang on a minute, these animal names are all mixed up! Split them up and put them back together properly to spell six real animals.

FER KEY

_____

MON SEL

_____

WAL TLE

_____

TUR VER

_____

WEA RUS

_____

BEA RET

_____

CITY SCAPE

Finish the buildings and add your own designs
to make a city you would love to explore.

YEE HAW!

Which of these two cowboys are exactly the same?

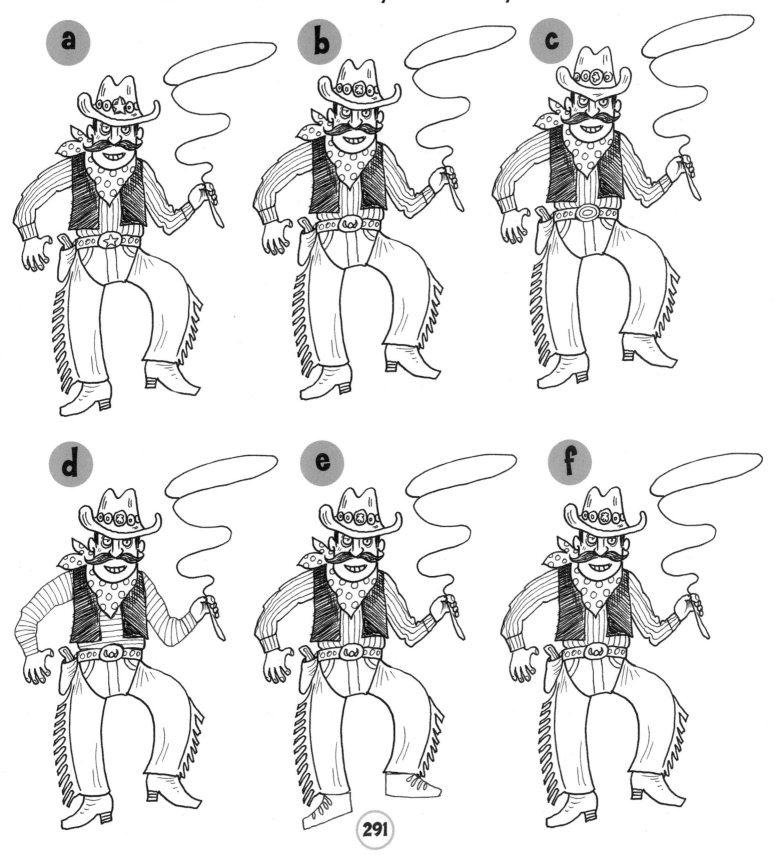

ROAD TRIP

Are we there yet?! Kill time by creating new words with three or more letters from the phrase below. One has been done to help you get started.

THIS IS BORING!

1. GHOST
2. _____
3. _____
4. _____
5. _____
6. _____
7. _____
8. _____
9. _____
10. _____

11. _____
12. _____
13. _____
14. _____
15. _____
16. _____
17. _____
18. _____
19. _____
20. _____

CHEMICAL CHAOS

If A = 1, B = 2, C=3 and so on, figure out what each of evil Doc Paradox's formulas is called.

2.18.19.14 2.12.1.19.20.5.18

4.9.19.1.16.16.5.1.18.9.15

13.5.7.1.2.5.12.3.8 10.21.9.3.5

293

NIGHT VISION

What kind of animal is peering at you from this page? Finish it yourself - make it cute, fierce, or totally freaky!

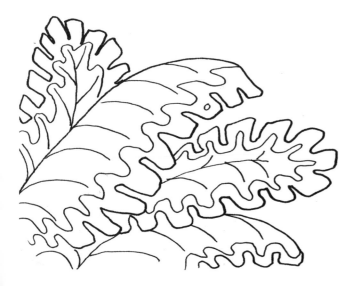

PETS ON PARADE

Which pet should replace the question mark to correctly complete the pattern?

a

b

c

d

STRANDED

Daisy Dolittle is stranded on top of the maze tower in Dubai! Only Spiderguy can help! Find a way up the building to rescue Daisy, and then climb back down the other side.

PUT IN THEIR PLACE

Add the pets to the sudoku grid so that every row, column,
and mini-grid contains only one of each type.

CITY SEARCH

Where is Vicky going on her special trip? Look along each row to find the one letter that appears in every city name. Find all six letters to spell her vacation destination.

Versailles	Avignon	Vienna	Vilnius	____
San Diego	Seville	Zagreb	Rome	____
Milan	Montreal	Dublin	Sydney	____
Lima	Sofia	Paris	Kingston	____
Cardiff	Valencia	Calais	Moscow	____
New York	Canberra	Prague	Seoul	____

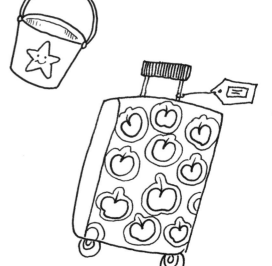

CATCHING CATTLE

These cattle have been branded to show who owns them.
Match each one to its owner by solving the equations.

$24 \div 6 =$

$72 \div 8 =$

$45 \div 9 =$

$54 \div 9 =$

$48 \div 6 =$

$49 \div 7 =$

SPORTS SEARCH

Look carefully in the grid to find fifteen sports that aren't quite as famous as others. They can be hidden across, up, down, and diagonally.

POLO	NETBALL	JUDO
FENCING	SOFTBALL	KARATE
LACROSSE	SURFING	SNOOKER
DIVING	BOULES	DRESSAGE
SQUASH	CLIMBING	HURLING

S	K	A	R	N	S	U	R	F	i	N	G
U	G	S	D	R	E	S	S	A	G	E	i
R	N	N	J	U	D	T	N	E	T	S	N
H	i	O	L	P	N	S	B	A	B	U	G
U	C	O	A	S	O	Q	R	A	C	R	N
R	N	K	C	S	O	A	A	J	L	L	i
L	E	E	R	E	K	S	J	U	L	L	B
i	F	R	O	R	E	H	V	D	i	A	M
N	E	T	S	D	i	V	i	N	G	B	i
G	J	H	S	A	U	Q	S	V	i	T	L
S	Q	U	E	P	B	O	U	L	D	F	C
J	U	D	D	R	E	S	S	O	L	O	P
P	O	L	B	O	U	L	E	S	Q	S	Q

300

CREATURE COUNT

Study this picture of the rainforest canopy and see how many of each creature you can count.

Butterflies = ☐   Snakes = ☐

Beetles = ☐   Birds = ☐

FALLING OR FLYING?

SuperPete is holding onto something - but is he flying or hitching a ride?
You decide - draw what's high in the sky with him.

GO, GINNY, GO!

Help Ginny the guinea pig find her way to her friends by following the arrows in the right direction each time.

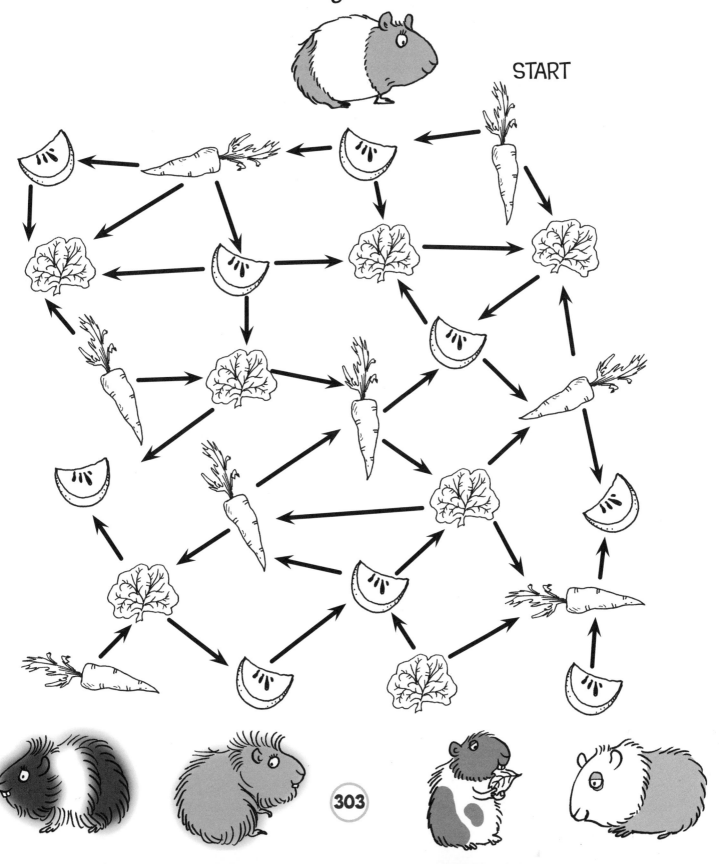

START

MUSCLE MAN

Use the grid references to write down the corresponding letters.
They will spell out what sport this muscle man competes in.

	a	b	c	d
4	i	D	L	P
3	A	R	O	M
2	G	U	W	T
1	E	K	S	N

c2 b3 a1 c1 d2 c4 a4 d1 a2

___ ___ ___ ___ ___ ___ ___ ___ ___

STABLE SHADOWS

Look carefully at the picture of Belinda with her pony.
Which of the silhouettes matches it exactly?

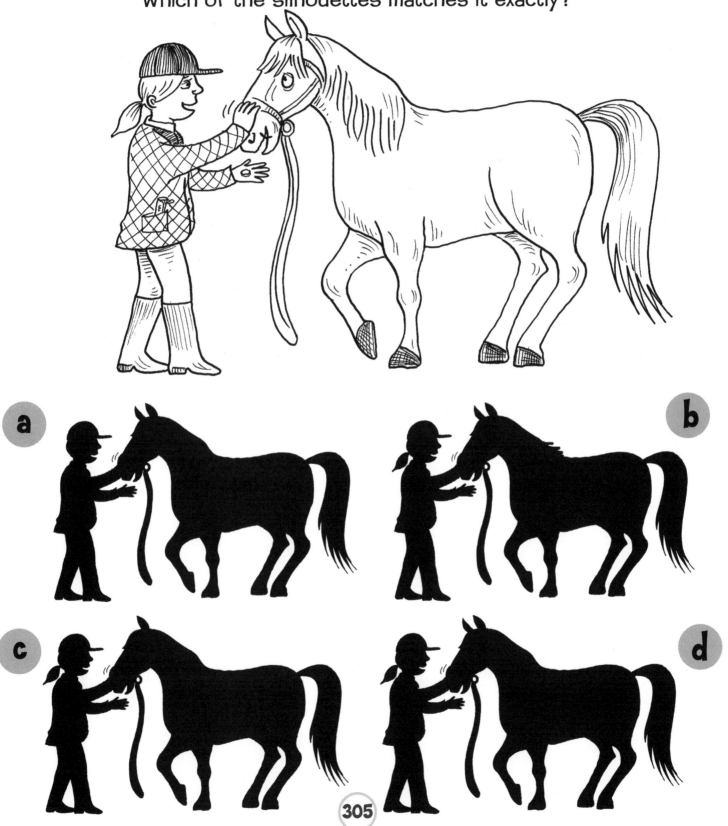

OFF WE GO!

Unscramble the letters on each luggage tag to find out which cities everyone is visiting on their travels.

New Zealand

Greece

Canada

Australia

Thailand

Egypt

BIRD'S EYE VIEW

Study the shootout picture, and then decide which of the smaller pictures
is the proper bird's eye view of the scene.

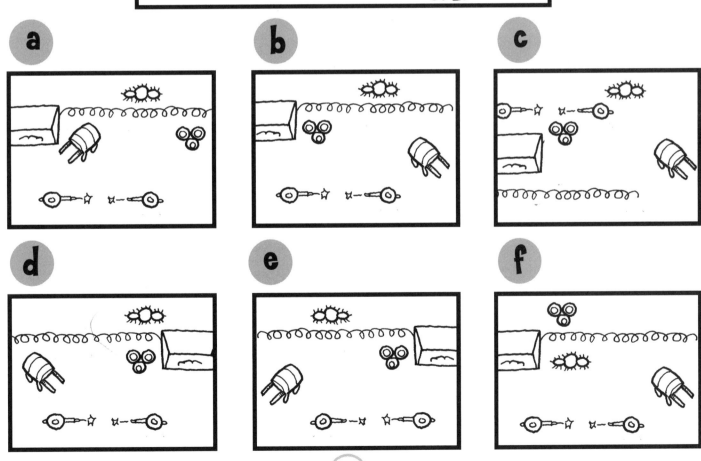

a

b

c

d

e

f

SPORTS CAMP

Find out what camp activities are scheduled at the times shown, using the unusual clock. Follow the instructions carefully.

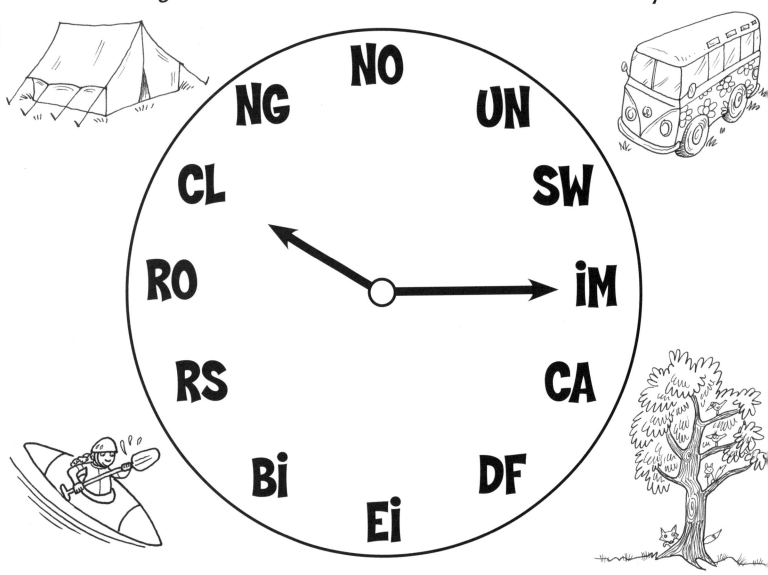

Write down the letters shown by the minute hand, then by the hour hand, for each time listed below. Together, they will spell the activities you are looking for. For example, ten past three = SWIM.

 a
ten to three
twenty-five to eleven

b
twenty past twelve
half past eleven

FOOTPRINTS

The mini-grid only appears once in the larger grid below.
Can you find it?

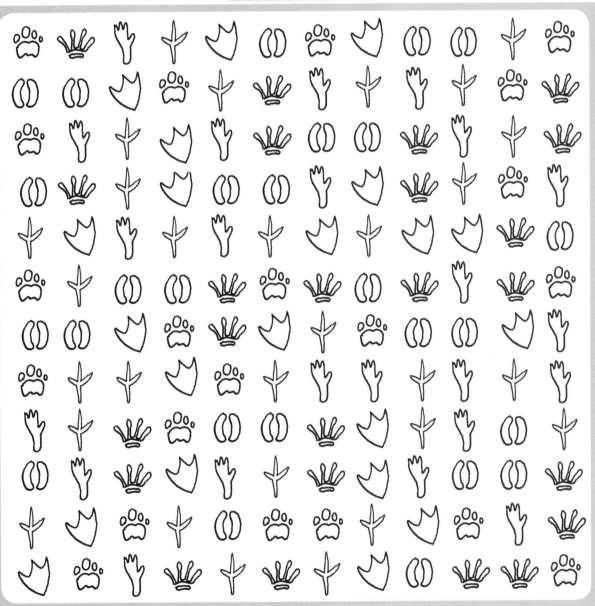

WHO LIVES HERE?

What sort of pet do you think lives here?

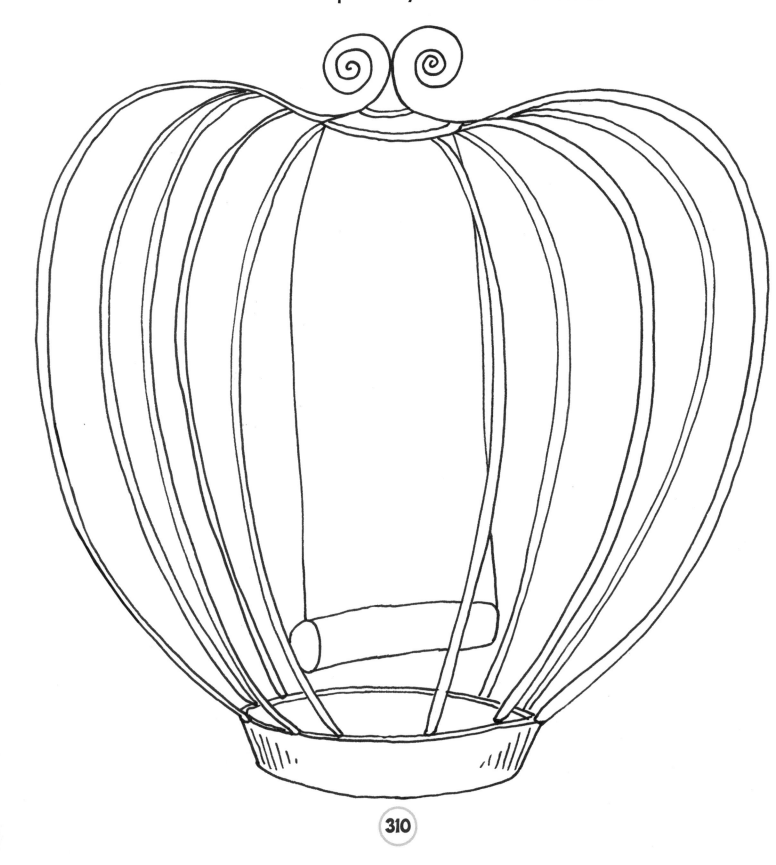

ANSWERS

3 CHEEKY MONKEYS
d

4 CAPITAL LETTERS
BELGIUM = Brussels
FINLAND = Helsinki
CHINA = Beijing
JAMAICA = Kingston
UNITED KINGDOM = London

5 A WALK IN THE PARK
1. Eating their picnic lunches **2.** D3
3. Reindeer   **4.** E1

6 UNDER COVER

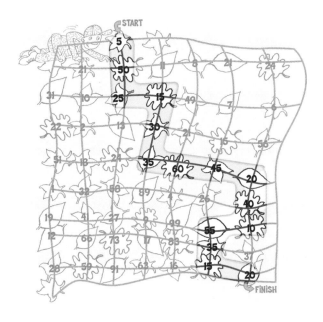

7 NUMBER CRUNCH
= 1   = 2
= 3   = 7

8 MONSTER MAD
c

9 HAUNTED HOUSE

10 TASTY TREATS
84

11 ANIMAL BREAKOUT
Code = 6324

12 PIRATE PARADE
b and e

13 ALPHADOKU

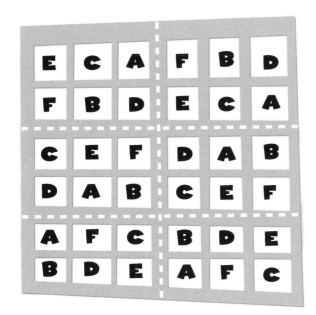

E	C	A	F	B	D
F	B	D	E	C	A
C	E	F	D	A	B
D	A	B	C	E	F
A	F	C	B	D	E
B	D	E	A	F	C

14 SPOT THE DIFFERENCE

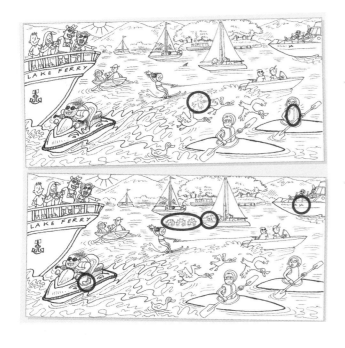

15 MENU MIX-UP

BANANA   BURGER
CARROT   ORANGE
PEANUT   SALMON
TOMATO   WAFFLE
TURKEY   POTATO

16 WORLD RECORDS

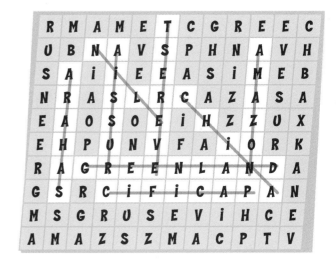

17 PLANET SIX

6, 12, 18, 24, 30, 36, 42, 48, 54, 60

18 ODD ONE OUT

f

19 GRIDLOCKED

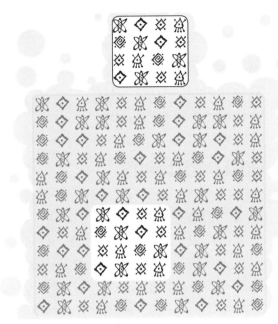

20 SOCCER SUMS

a = 2   b = 5

c = 3   d = 4

e = 6

22 CLASS ACT

1. The Solar System
2. Man
3. 5
4. 10:30
5. Flowers
6. 2
7. Fish
8. 3
9. Spots
10. Fish-shaped

23 FAIRY TALES

Here are some you might have thought of:

one, pat, tea, cat, put, none, pout, pint, cone, open, tape, meat, pounce, peanut, coupon

24 SUDOKU

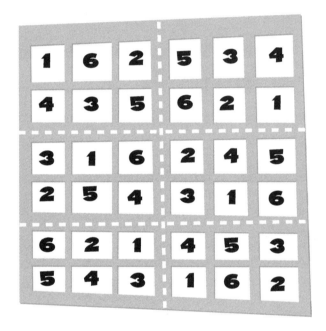

25 OUT OF ORDER

2, 6, 1, 3, 4, 5

26 TREASURE HUNT

C1 - by the cacti

27 DOUBLE TROUBLE
Pelican; swallow
Vulture; peacock
Ostrich; chicken
Penguin; sparrow

28 TIGER TABLES

29 DINO-DETECTIVE
IGUANODON

30 PLANE SAILING
c

31 ON THE MOVE
Bicycle; tractor; yacht;
train; plane;
speedboat; motorcycle;
helicopter

32 FEEDING FRENZY
e

33 ZOO SHOPPING
1. $7
2. 4
3. 2 snow globes ($8)
4. $1

34 ALPHADOKU

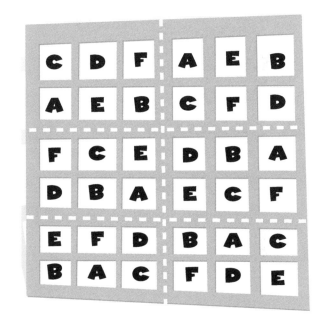

35 WHAT NEXT?
c

36 AT THE POOL
d

37 AT THE GAME

38 BUGOKU

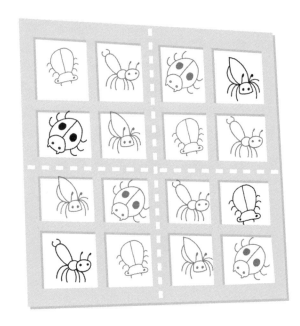

39 MOON WALK

40 THIRSTY WORK

f

41 A DAY AT THE ZOO

42 FOOD FOR THOUGHT

SANDWICH

LAMB CHOP

FISH CAKE

43 AT THE AIRPORT

Find these!

44 GRIDLOCKED

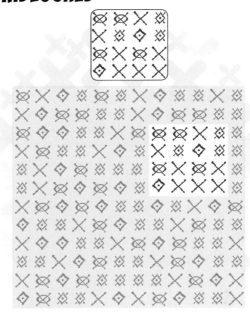

45 SPY SCHOOL
South America

46 FEEDING TIME
Code = 1635

47 CAMPSITE CHALLENGE

48 SPACED OUT
Uranus; Jupiter; Mercury;
Neptune; Asteroid; Meteor

49 BUGOKU

50 SPY SCHOOL
WHAT WORKS UNDERCOVER,
SPEAKS MANY LANGUAGES,
AND HAS EIGHT LEGS?
A SPY-DER!

51 PIECES OF EIGHT
a

52 SNACK SUMS

🥧 = 1   🍦 = 2

🍎 = 4   🍦 = 6

53 DOUBLE TROUBLE
Fencing; cycling
Skating; surfing
Baseball; climbing
Softball; swimming

54 FOURASAURUS
4, 8, 12, 16, 20, 24, 28, 32, 36,
40, 44, 48

55 BLAST OFF!
e

56 RIGGING RIDDLE
MAST-MALT-MALL-MAIL-SAIL

57 NUMBER MAZE

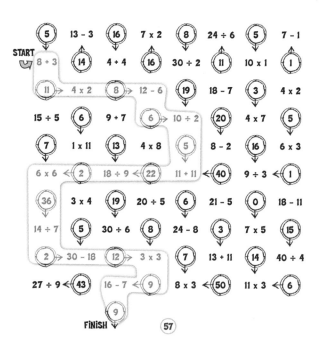

58 ELEPHANT RIDE

e

59 ANIMAL MIX-UP

MONKEY
JAGUAR
MARMOT
GERBIL
GIBBON
COYOTE
BADGER
TURTLE
PYTHON
WALRUS

60 ALPHADOKU

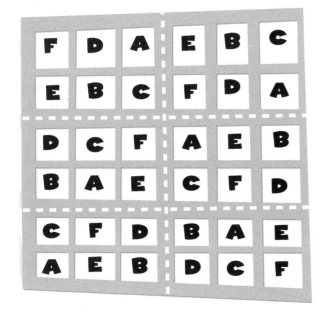

61 STATION SLEUTH

1. 3
2. 3:13
3. Paris
4. 3
5. Reading a newspaper (or pretending to!)
6. Right
7. Lips
8. Books
9. Guitar
10. 1 and 2

63 FAIRY DUST

c and e

64 ENDANGERED SPECIES

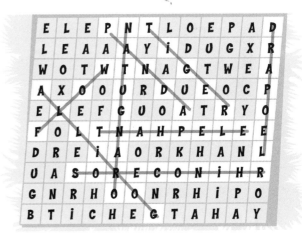

65 A BUG'S LIFE

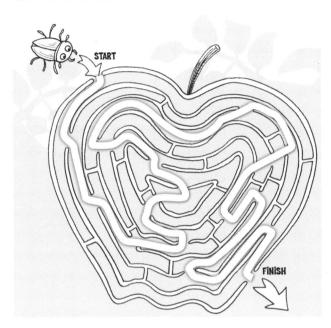

66 NUMBER CRUNCH

67 OLYMPIC GAMES

1. Hockey
2. A5
3. D5
4. Basketball

68 JET SETTERS

Here are some you might have thought of:

dad, wet, two, owl, nut, tear, deal, down, hurt, wear, lead, heard, learn, under, throw

69 MAGICAL MARVIN

70 RIDE 'EM COWBOY!

d

71 FOODOKU

72 FLOWER FAIRIES

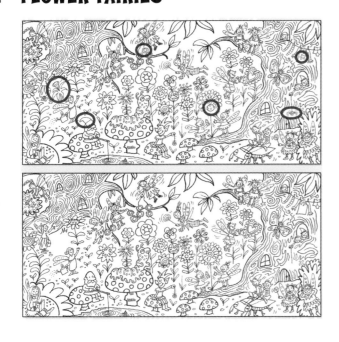

73 SPY SCHOOL
GO TO THE LIBRARY

74 SEA LIFE SQUARES
Lobster; dolphin

75 CRAZY CRABS

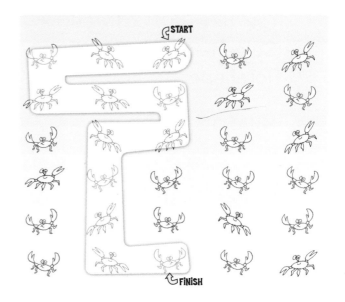

76 MAP MIX-UP
MEXICO   FRANCE
CANADA   TURKEY
SWEDEN   POLAND
ISRAEL   RUSSIA
GREECE   KUWAIT

77 MONSTER TRUCK
d

78 TAKING A TRIP

Flight tickets:	3 x $100 =	$300
Suitcases:	4 x $10 =	$40
Train tickets:	3 x $60 =	$180
Car hire:	1 x $40 =	$40
Splashworld:	2 x $5 =	$10
Total spent:		$570

79 WHAT TO WEAR?

e

80 CLIMBING THE WALL

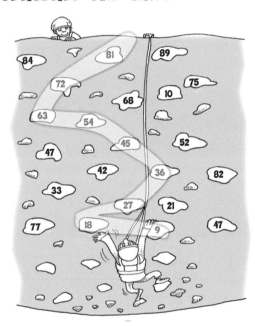

81 TIDY UP TIME

52 leaves; 9 bugs

82 SPOT THE DIFFERENCE

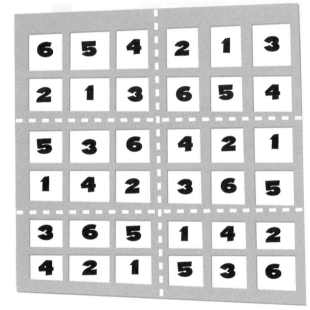

83 SUDOKU

84 COOL CALCULATIONS
3 treats @ $0.50 = $1.50
2 treats @ $0.90 = $1.80
3 ice creams @ $0.75 = $2.25
2 treats @ $0.65 = $1.30
Total = $6.85

85 IN THE LAB
a

86 TROPICAL PARADISE

87 SPY SCHOOL
WHAT DID THE SPY SAY WHEN
HE GOT STUCK IN SEAWEED?

"KELP! KELP!"

88 OUT OF ORDER
3, 5, 6, 2, 1, 4

89 GRIDLOCKED

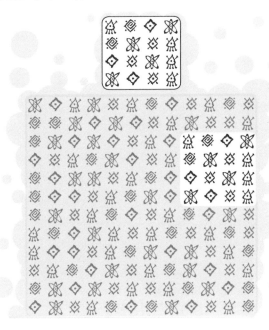

90 JEWEL THIEF
3964

91 FLYING FUN
1. 9
2. Flying
3. 2
4. 3
5. Stripes
6. Hot dogs and ice cream
7. 8
8. Saturday
9. 6
10. 2

93 DELICIOUS DESSERTS
b and f

94 BUGOKU
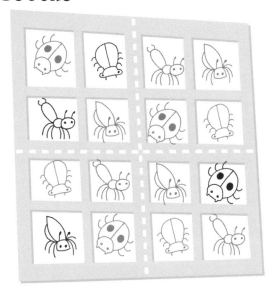

95 TREASURE HUNT

96 CREEPY CRAWLIES
BUMBLEBEE
BEETLE
CENTIPEDE
BUTTERFLY

97 FIRE DRILL
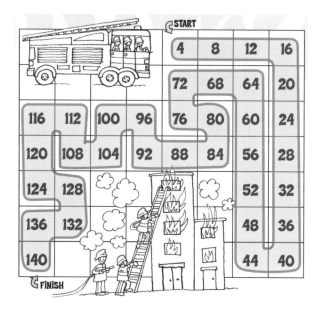

98 LIBRARY CODES
Geography books

99 PLAY TIME

100 ALPHADOKU

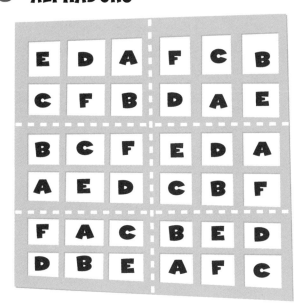

101 TOTALLY TROPICAL
40

102 PARTY BAGS
1. Toy lizard ($1.00)
   Stars x 2 ($0.20)
   Elephant ($0.50)
   Total: $1.70
2. Hat ($2.50)
   Lollipop ($0.75)
   Pencil ($0.75)
   Total: $4.00
3. Hat ($2.50)
   Star ($0.10)
   Elephant ($0.50)
   Pencil ($0.75)
   Lizard ($1.00)
   Lollipop ($0.75)
   Total: $5.60

103 FANTASTIC GYMNASTICS

104 SUMMER OLYMPICS

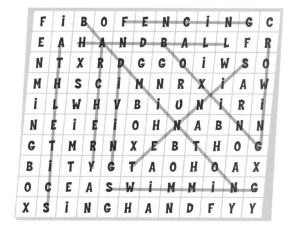

105 WHAT NEXT?
b

106 CASTLE CAPERS
1. Church   2. D4
3. E3   4. Horses

107 SPY SCHOOL

Knock! Knock!
Who's there?
Sadie...
Sadie who?
Sadie secret code or you
can't come in!

108 CHILL-OUT TIME

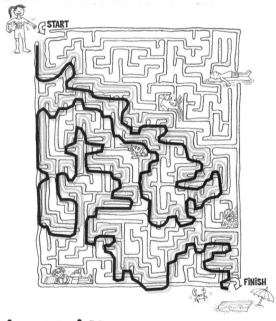

109 BIRD BRAINS

TOUCAN
CONDOR
MAGPIE
PIGEON
FALCON
PARROT
THRUSH
TURKEY
PUFFIN
CUCKOO

110 SPOT THE DIFFERENCE

111 FOODOKU

326

112 RAINY-DAY PUZZLE
Here are some you might have thought of: **din, ran, son, acid, sign, gong, grin, again, drain, grain, grant, snort, short, string, training**

113 FAIRY TALE
d

114 NUMBER CRUNCH

 = 3   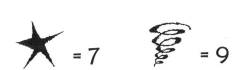 = 6

★ = 7   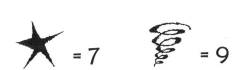 = 9

115 DINO CLUB
a

116 POP PUZZLER

117 OCTOPLUS
8562

118 TREASURE HUNT

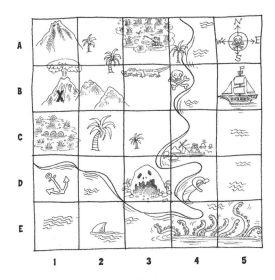

119 SPY SCHOOL
WHAT DO YOU CALL A SPY WHO HIDES AT THE BEACH? SANDY!

120 IN A TWIRL
8, 16, 24, 32, 40, 48, 56, 64, 72, 80, 88, 96

121 BEAUTIFUL BUTTERFLIES
e

122 SUDOKU

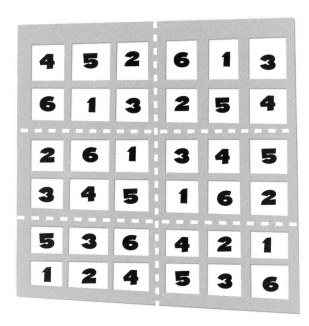

123 FAST FOOD FRAZZLER

1. 3
2. Man
3. A teddy bear
4. Burger and hot dog
5. 2
6. Woman
7. 2
8. 3
9. A train
10. 2

125 GRIDLOCKED

126 FIRE STARTERS
a and e

127 OUT OF ORDER
4, 3, 6, 2, 5, 1

128 SHOPPING TRIP
1. D1
2. C1
3. Clothes store
4. E3

129 SNAIL TRAIL

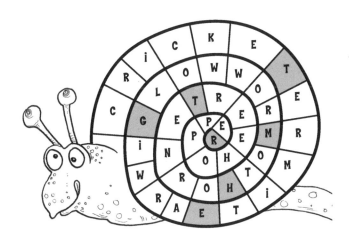

130 ROLL THE DICE
462 + 135 = 597
124 + 632 = 756
541 + 123 = 664
653 + 154 = 807
246 + 645 + 891

131 JUNGLE FEVER
BY THE TARANTULAS

132 CIRCUS SEVENS

133 WITCH NEXT?
b

134 SPOT THE DIFFERENCE

135 NUMBER CRUNCH

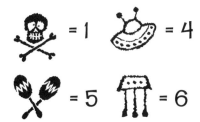

136 CAMPING TRIP
HIKE-BIKE-BAKE-CAKE-CAME-CAMP

137 GHASTLY GHOSTS
31 ghosts; 11 bats

138 PARTY PUZZLE

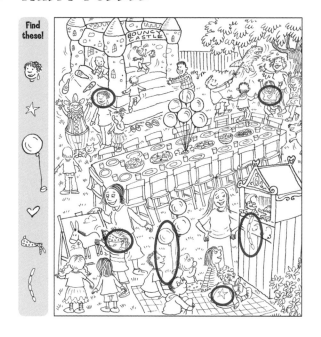

Find these!

139 PAINTER'S PALETTE

Orange, violet, scarlet

140 ALL CHANGE

c

141 FLYING FARTHEST

The top plane has flown the farthest (68 compared to 55 and 59)

142 FOODOKU

143 TRACK SIDE

144 HIDDEN GNOMES

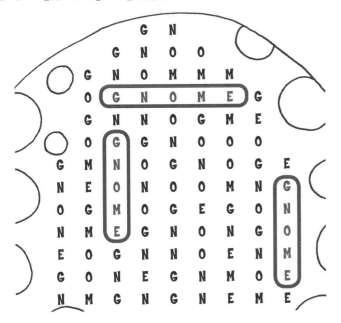

145 TEEPEE TEASER

f

146 FARMER BEN'S HEN

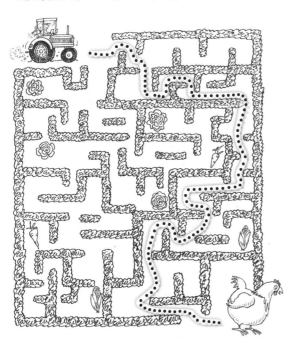

147 EATEN EIGHTS

11 apples

148 JUNGLE TREASURE

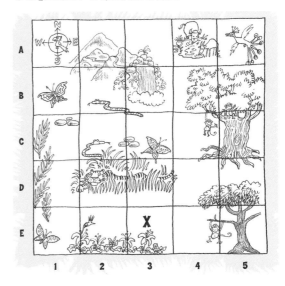

149 BUGOKU

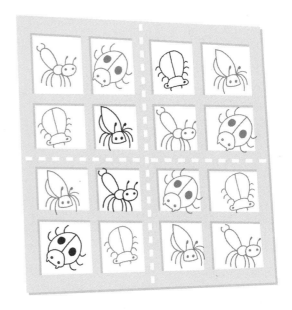

150 BEAT THE TEACHER

The answer is 126

151 OUTDOOR FUN
a

152 PET CITY

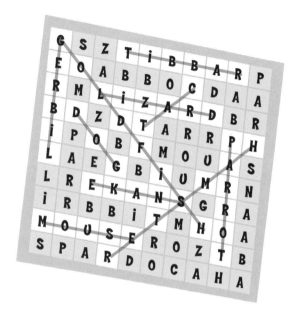

153 FANCY THAT!

154 TROPHY CABINET

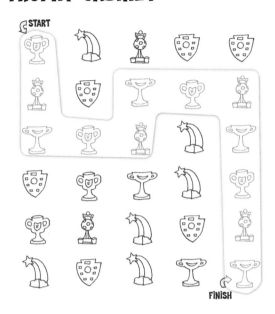

155 JURASSIC PARK
Here are some you might
have thought of:
**pod, cup, lip, cod, old, lid, oil,
clip, idol, dodo, cold, loud, cool,
soup, solid**

156 SPY SCHOOL
WHY DID THE SILLY SPY
GO TO NIGHT SCHOOL?
HE WANTED TO LEARN TO
READ IN THE DARK.

157 AT THE BALLET
c and f

158 SKI RUN
11, 22, 33, 44, 55, 66, 77, 88,
99, 110

159 WALKING THE DOG

160 GREEK ODYSSEY

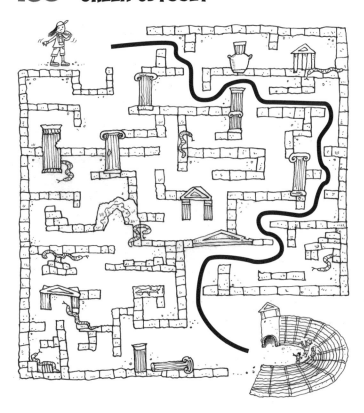

161 COWBOY CRACKER

It was a little hoarse

162 SLALOM SCORE

a = 41

b = 38

164 SIX PACK

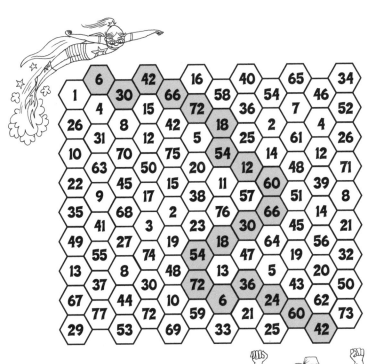

165 MOUSE TRAP

166 DESTINATION UNKNOWN
LISBON
LONDON
DUBLIN
HAVANA
VIENNA
WARSAW

167 RODEO RIDER
c

168 ON THE BALL
Volleyball

169 PENGUIN PARADE
i

170 A PRICKLY PROBLEM
c

172 TIME FOR A TRIP
Thailand, Barbados

173 CROSS-EYED
14

174 BULLSEYE
a = 44
b = 34
c = 34

175 SUPERBAD

Krall the Conqueror

176 SETTING UP HOME

c, b, a

177 BEST IN SHOW

Here are some you might
have thought of:

Sew, zip, press, rest, stir,
strip, new, spit, swept, persist,
wise, size, wet, rip, net

178 SWEET TREATS

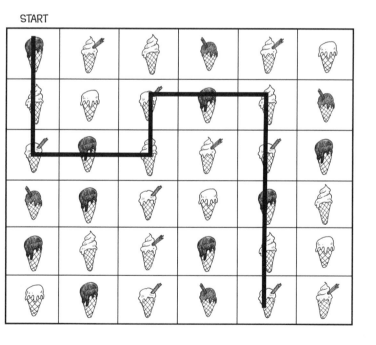

180 ALL-TIME GREATS

1. Cycling
2. Fencing
3. Swimming
4. Athletics
5. Gymnastics

181 PERFECT PRIMATES

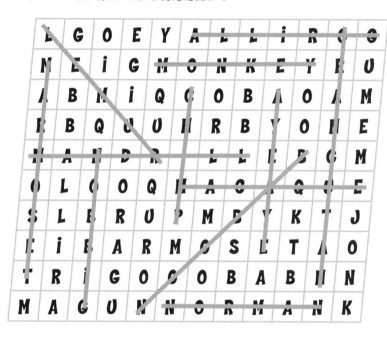

182 GONE IN A FLASH

e

183 PET PANDEMONIUM

8 pets are missing.

185 SHERIFF'S SUDOKU

186 SPORTS SORT

Boxing glove - boxing glove
Bowling ball - bowling pin
Helmet - bicycle
Cricket bat - stumps
Ice hockey stick - puck
Arrow - bow
Tennis ball - tennis racquet
Table tennis bat - ball

187 PAW PRINTS

Lion, wolf, skunk, lynx

188 COMIC STRIP

f, c, e, a, d, b

189 BRAIN TEASER

Carl owns a gerbil named Hector.
Susie owns a pony named Crystal.
Grace owns a cat named Peppa.

190 CHOCOHOLICS

191 SPOON SEARCH

There are ten spoons.

193 "C" CREATURES

Here are ten; did you think
of any more?

**Camel, coyote, canary, crocodile,
cow, cheetah, cat, chimpanzee,
chicken, chameleon.**

194 A COOL CLIMBER

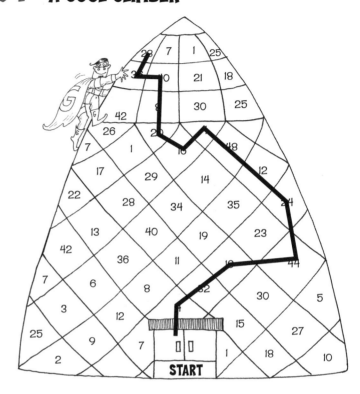

195 YOU CHOOSE

196 IN A STATE

The hidden state is Indiana.

A	R	i	Z	O	N	A
N	E	W	Y	O	R	K
F	L	O	R	i	D	A
W	Y	O	M	i	N	G
A	L	A	B	A	M	A
M	O	N	T	A	N	A
G	E	O	R	G	i	A

197 QUICK ON THE DRAW

198 CROSS OUT

In case he got a hole in one

199 SAFARI TRAIL

201 A TRICKY QUESTION

Hercules

202 TRAIN TREK

1. 10:41
2. 7 hours 15 minutes
3. 4:35
4. The 7:45 from Paris is slowest.
5. 1 hour 55 minutes

203 SAY WHAT?

Saddle up and hit the trail.

204 EXTREME THRILLS

e

205 STINKY SUMS

206 ON THE MOVE

Mindreading

207 COLLARED

10

209 THE WILD WEST

1. E3
2. Groceries
3. The cemetery
4. C5

210 BOUNCE AROUND

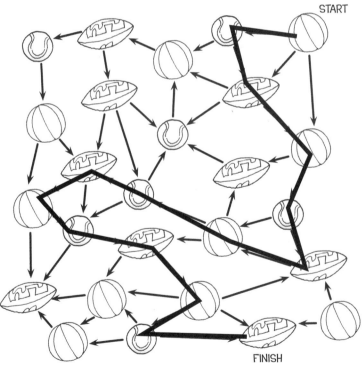

211 CRITTER LITTERS

53 - 46 = 7 (wild boar)

(12 x 12) - 132 = 12 (crocodile)

(9 x 9) - 80 = 1 (monkey)

45 ÷ 5 = 9 (wolf)

60 ÷ 12 = 5 (lion)

(8 x 6) ÷ 24 = 2 (polar bear)

212 FLYING HIGH

b

213 PET PUZZLER

214 CAUGHT ON CAMERA

215 BEHIND BARS

1 = 5

2 = 7

3 = 9

4 = 3

216 ANYONE FOR TENNIS?

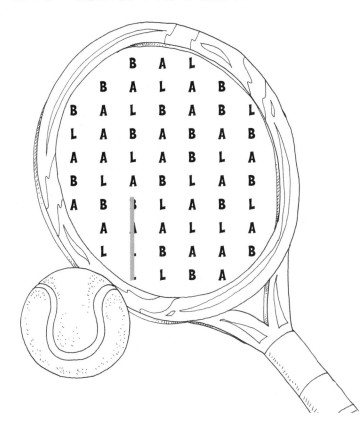

```
  B A L
B A L A B
B A L B A B L
L A B A B A B
A A L A B L A B
B L A B L A B
A B   L A B L
A   A L L A B
L   B A A B
    L B A
```

218 SUPER TROOPER

Invisibility

219 FLY AWAY HOME

1 = c
2 = b
3 = a

220 LOST LUGGAGE

d

221 WAGON WHEELS

a. cactus
b. saddle
c. desert
d. cattle
e. lizard
f. bullet

222 SLAM DUNK

223 LEAPING LEMURS!

226 CYPRUS SUDOKU

224 SUPER SPELLINGS

Here are some you might
have thought of:
Cover, selves, love, sir,
cress, resolve, elves, lose, verse,
cross, vile, serve,
core, recess, veer, sole

227 AMBUSHED!

228 PARK LIFE
1. D2
2. Archery
3. A3
4. C2
5. Tennis
6. D5

229 CUTE CUBS
d

230 ON THE RUN
Cape, gloves,
boots, suit,
mask, belt.
The villain's name
is Paradox.

231 NETTED

232 RIDING HIGH

234 STICK WITH IT

30

235 SSSSSSILLY SSSSSSTUFF

It got lockjaw

236 SUPER SHOOTERS

Strength

237 JUST JOKING

Because they have nine lives

238 CIAO ITALIA!

Pisa, Rome, Milan, Naples

239 POWWOW, NOW!

c

241 EAGLE EYES

a. D2

b. H8

c. G1

d. E6

e. A5

f. B2

242 BETTER, FASTER, HIGHER

a = 152

b = 151

c = 151

243 IT'S A MYSTERY

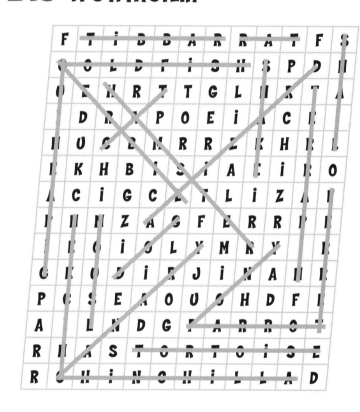

244 FUN IN THE SUN

245 PICK A POLE
g

246 BOWLED OVER
71

247 TIME TO EAT!
a = elephant
b = kangaroo

249 MUCKING OUT

250 ON THE CASE
1645

251 THE OLD WEST
Utah

252 ON YOUR BIKE

Cross country

253 BIRD BRAINS

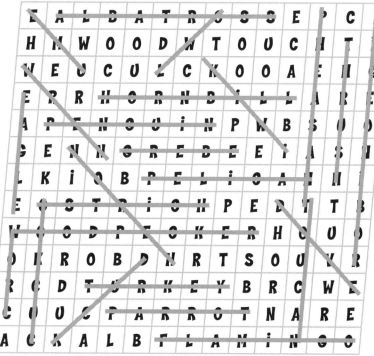

254 JEWEL THIEF

The Jade Assassin

255 DOG TIRED

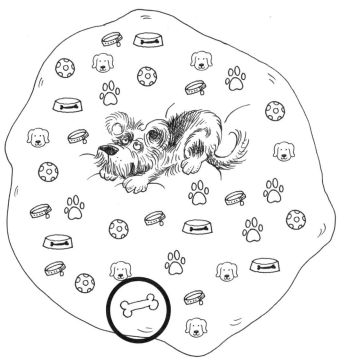

257 HOME SWEET HOME

a. D2

b. B1

c. B7

d. E8

e. H6

f. E3

258 ALL THE BALLS

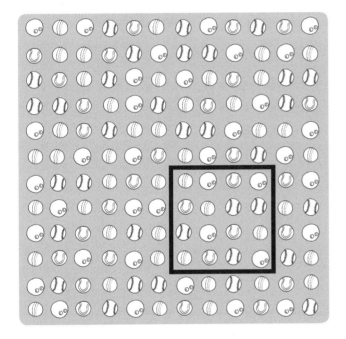

259 ROLL UP, ROLL UP!

23

260 UNDERWATER RESCUE

a and e

261 FUNNY BUNNIES

e

262 DREAM TICKET

Florida Keys

263 SADDLE UP

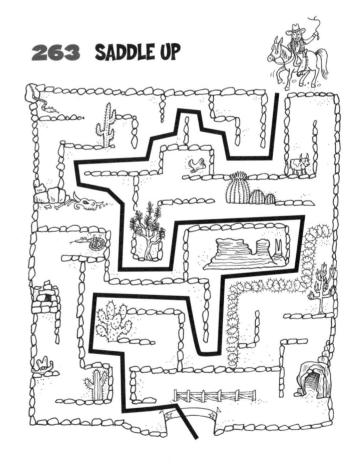

264 GOING FOR GOLD

Usain Bolt

266 BOO! HISS!

d

267 CUDDLY CREATURES

1. Peacock
2. A3
3. C4
4. E5
5. Piglets
6. Llamas

268 GET PACKING

The paired items are:
flip flops, bucket (pail)
and spade, face mask and
snorkel, notepad and pen,
toothbrush and toothpaste.

269 THE LONE RANGER

R	A	N	G	G	E	R	E	E	G
A	R	E	G	A	N	A	N	R	A
N	A	N	G	R	A	N	A	A	G
E	N	A	E	N	E	N	G	N	R
R	A	R	R	G	A	E	A	R	E
A	A	E	M	E	G	R	A	N	G
R	E	G	A	N	G	R	A	N	R
E	G	N	E	E	G	A	E	G	E
R	A	G	E	R	N	E	N	E	E
G	R	E	G	A	N	A	R	G	N

270 SPORTS SQUARE

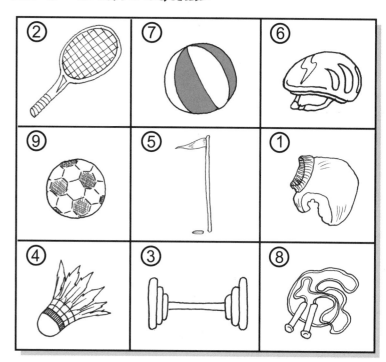

②	⑦	⑥
⑨	⑤	①
④	③	⑧

348

271 LION LAUGHS
He tasted funny

272 TO THE RESCUE!
There are ten party horns.

274 LADY LIBERTY
e

275 THE SILVER SADDLE
a. D5
b. F2
c. C2
d. B7
e. H6
f. B8

276 COACH GOODWAY
f - he coaches gymnastics

277 TALL AND SMALL

278 HELP ME!

279 BIRD TALK
Australia

280 SNORKEL SCARE
e, f, a, c, b, d

282 WIN OR LOSE?
Because he kept drawing!

283 ICE, ICE BABY

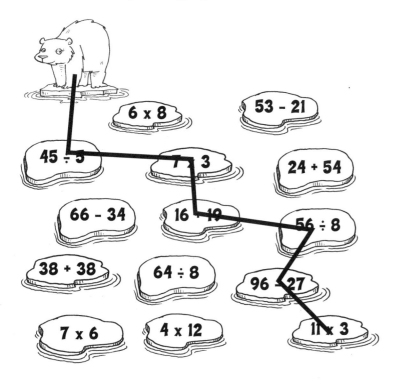

284 SUPERFOODS
Blueberry pie

285 IT'S A STICK UP
12

286 BIG ADVENTURE
Amy is going to France
in a teepee.
Leigh is going to Spain in a tent.

Millie is going to Italy
in a camper van.

287 OUTLAWED
They should look behind
wild cat mountain (D6).

289 ANIMAL MIX-UP!
Ferret, monkey, walrus, turtle,
weasel, beaver

291 YEE HAW!
b and f

292 ROAD TRIP
Here are some you
might have thought of:
Big, snort, rot, hiss, stir,
torn, north, short, shirt,
insist, boss, hot, rib, right,
tin, sob, night, orb, thin, sit.

293 CHEMICAL CHAOS
BRAIN BLASTER, DISAPPEARIO,
MEGABELCH JUICE

295 PETS ON PARADE
d

296 STRANDED

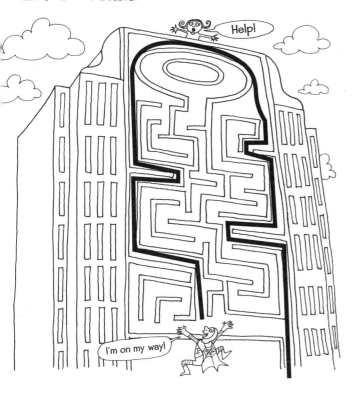

297 PUT IN THEIR PLACE

298 CITY SEARCH

Venice

299 CATCHING CATTLE

24 ÷ 6 = 4

72 ÷ 8 = 9

48 ÷ 6 = 8

54 ÷ 9 = 6

45 ÷ 9 = 5

49 ÷ 7 = 7

300 SPORTS SEARCH

S	K	A	R	N	S	U	R	F	i	N	G
U	G	S	D	R	E	S	S	A	G	E	i
R	N	N	J	U	D	T	N	E	T	S	N
M	O	L	P	N	S	L	A	B	U	G	G
O	G	O	A	S	O	Q	K	A	C	R	I
R	N	K	S	O	A	A	J	A	L	E	I
L	E	E	R	E	K	S	J	U	L	I	B
I	R	O	R	E	H	V	D	i	A	I	
N	E	T	S	D	i	V	i	N	G		
G	U	H	A	U	G	S	V	i	T	L	
S	Q	U	E	P	B	O	U	L	D	I	C
J	U	D	P	R	E	S	S	O	L	A	P
P	O	L	B	O	U	L	E	S	Q	S	Q

301 CREATURE COUNT
Butterflies = 15
Beetles = 10
Snakes = 6
Birds = 8

303 GO, GINNY, GO!

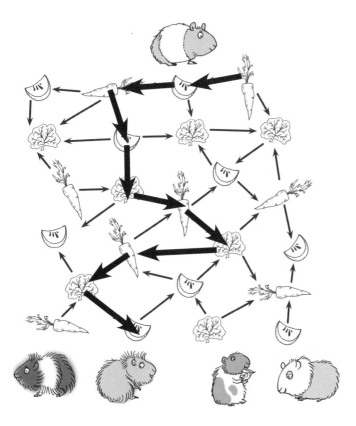

304 MUSCLE MAN
Wrestling

305 STABLE SHADOWS
d

306 OFF WE GO!
Auckland, New Zealand
Athens, Greece
Toronto, Canada
Sydney, Australia
Bangkok, Thailand
Cairo, Egypt

307 BIRD'S EYE VIEW
b

308 SPORTS CAMP
a = climbing
b = canoeing

309 FOOTPRINTS

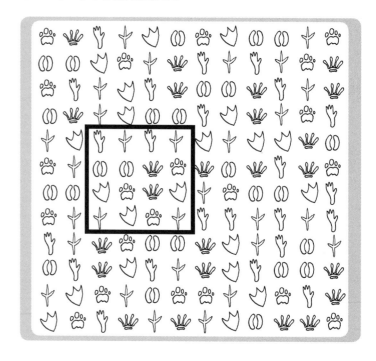